The MILKMAN Story

What Happens When a Jewish Carpenter Meets a Gentile Milkman

PAUL ROBBINS

ANM publishers

THE MILKMAN STORY

ISBN: 978-0-9794929-8-3 Paperback

Published by:

Advancing Native Missions
P.O. Box 5303 • Charlottesville, VA 22905
www.AdvancingNativeMissions.com

Cover and Interior Design by:
Heather Kirk
www.GFSstudio.com

Milk Crate Drawing by:
Don Whitson
www.DonWhitson-art.com

To Marla

The more I get to know myself, the more amazed I am that you are still here. You have remained loyal for the past forty-two years and counting. I have dragged you through the dust of many dreams and visions, yet your trust has allowed my failures to appear as footsteps in the seemingly unending process of this book. Thank you for allowing love to believe the unlikely.

ACKNOWLEDGEMENTS

For Rob Hewitt, you heard me speak so highly of Pastor Al for years and had the foresight to see the need to put it in writing.

Then you had the humility to step back from professionally doing it. Instead you became my personal trainer and instilled courage in me to write what I never dreamed I could.

For Donna and Pat who read the rough draft and actually saw potential. For Dara who went way beyond the professional veneer of proofreader and added so much more life to the project.

For Virginia who has invested more energy and enthusiasm into my random compilation than I ever could have expected, you have convinced me that this book should be read. Even more, you added wisdom in so many subtle ways that the "natural became the supernatural."

For Heather and Christopher, you were in the midst of painful struggles yet in pursuit of God, said yes to add His creative signature.

For Don Whitson, thank you for being willing to enter swiftly into my dilemma. With artistic skill and selfless generosity, you brought a beautiful solution.

And over and above, for Jesus, my Messiah, You have put all of us together to reach someone who has yet to be affected. He or she may even skip this part (like I normally do), but is now on the edge of discovery. May this story bring liberation and determination to be lead by Your Spirit into a life made new.

For in the end, this story must be about You.

TABLE OF CONTENTS

PREFACE

Searching For Authenticity

I do not go grocery shopping very often, perhaps on occasion for a few needs, but certainly not for the entire week. It would take too long. When I stroll down the aisles of the supermarket, I am still in awe of the many choices that I encounter for each item on the shopping list. I consider it my duty as a representative of my family to bring home the best product at the best price. That is the dilemma. The comparisons are overwhelming.

I remember my father, who loved to shop, using the expression, "You have to compare apples to apples." Well, that may have been a bit easier back then, but now even comparing apples is a daunting task. In one display there may be apples ranging in color from light yellow to dark green and every shade of red. They come from everywhere—New Zealand to Peru and from all across the United States. Some are in bags, some in baskets. Others are in piles with the DNA markings of dozens of people before me. One row says "organic," and another is so waxed and shiny that the fruit looks like furniture. Two of them are labeled "delicious," but has someone I know ever tasted them? I can buy three organic ones or three pounds of shiny ones for the same price, but a few days later when I eat one for lunch, it tastes like nothing and sometimes worse than nothing. It is quite a conundrum when I am standing there weighing my decision, my hands gripped tightly around the red plastic handle of an empty shopping cart and I am still four aisles away from the cereal section. At any moment my cell phone will ring. My wife will be on the other end wondering why I am not home yet.

I know that not everyone fits into the same category as I, and that is a good thing. I have come to realize that my food shopping experience is not really about reading labels and doing the math on price versus quantity ratios, but it is a search for authenticity. The search is really one in which I am looking for something that I can come home with that is beneficial to my family and was worth the exchange that I made with my family's money. I want them to not only trust me with what I bring through the door, but to share in my excitement that what I have is good. The problem that I encounter is that the claims that I read on the labels of the bottles, boxes, and jars are self-proclaiming. According to each of them, I have finally found that which I have been seeking. Could they all be true?

It is the same situation I found when I looked into the world of religion. With each religious product I purchased, I found something lacking in substance or in flavor or both.

My problem in the grocery aisle was parallel to my shopping experience in the spiritual aisle. The product claims sounded alike.

Peace, Joy, Nirvana.

Basically they were saying, "All products lead to the same Cashier at check-out time."

What I really needed in both circumstances was not one more product on the shelf, but someone who had a personal experience with the object on my shopping list. Be it a can of tomato sauce or the road to bliss, I needed somebody who could say, "I know exactly what will satisfy"—someone I could trust.

However, that posed another problem. Trust. How does one trust that another person's opinion will become your own? What if there is some self-interest involved, say, his last name is Macintosh or Kellogg? I needed someone with whom I could experience a deep sense of trust, especially when I was in the market for eternal life. I had been up and down those aisles numerous times only to go home, and after a season or two, realize that I had been sold a bill of goods and not the item advertised.

I grew up in a Jewish home. Both of my parents were Jewish. Most Gentiles out there will not understand this, but the Jewish reader will. My father was a Jewish atheist, and my mother was a Jewish agnostic. My mother came from an Orthodox family; my father came from the non-practicing side of Judaism. They met in the middle and raised us as Conservative Jews. Neither of them really believed that God had a clue what we were doing here. My mother was more superstitious than religious, so she believed that we had to be bar mitzvahed. She also believed that we had to celebrate Passover and fast on Yom Kippur.

So off the children went to Hebrew school. We would go twice a week after school in addition to a mandatory Saturday morning service. The Saturday service was dependent upon a "minyan" though: ten Jewish men in attendance.

Not such an easy feat on a Saturday morning in the unbelieving suburbs of Long Island.

However, someone would get on the phone and begin calling down the list of everyone in the Men's Club until they found one who could not come up with an adequate excuse. Meanwhile, my friends and I would be wishing and crossing our fingers (not praying) that no man would show up. I do not know how much time God allowed, or that the rabbis assumed God allowed, but He must have been long-suffering, because some-one always showed up and the service went on.

I suppose you could rightfully assume that I did not grow up in a believing community.

In fact, we would more realistically fall into the category of "gastronomic Jews" than any other.

We loved bagels and lox and whitefish.

My father was even more extreme. He would have eaten chopped liver at every meal.

However, when it came to believing that Judaism had all the answers to eternal life, I wonder how few stopped to consider. Hear me out, though; I had a good family. I loved my parents and my relatives, but as far as seeing life beyond Grandpa, it wasn't a thought.

For me, though, it was different. As a child I had dreams I could not explain. I would dream about the infinite and the infinitesimal. In the dream all things would grow endlessly larger and then endlessly diminish. In those dreams, all of the universe, of which I was a part, would grow and grow and expand beyond measure, and then it would begin to shrink and shrink until it was too small to see; but it was always as real as it ever was. Then it would start over. Those dreams seemed more real to me than when I was awake at times. Sound weird? Welcome to my world. The fact is I knew that this life was a small part of something much bigger, and it lasted much longer. I assumed that adults understood that and would tell me about it, but they didn't. I suppose that was the beginning of my search for the authentic. Deep inside I wanted a livable explanation, with no artificial color or flavor.

I did not see it in my Jewish community. It was not that love was missing or we had no community, because we did. We were Jewish. We were different. Our roots went deep into the world's history, and I was proud of being a Jew. Yet we had no depth. I didn't get it. What little I did learn was that nobody I knew took God as seriously as Abraham or Moses seemed to have done. It appeared to me that the Judaism the rabbis were teaching was nothing as adventurous as the Judaism that Abraham inherited.

And why all the suffering, the hatred toward us, and why did people think we were so different?

I never asked those questions and no one ever addressed them. It was just the way it was.

But I was adventurous, and my journeys as a boy took me to my neighbors' yards.

One day I was playing curb ball in front of the house of a Catholic family who lived on the corner. They had about nine kids, so there was always someone to play with.

Once in a while the oldest sister, Claudia, joined us. She always seemed to be smiling.

She never told me why she was happy, but I guess I never asked. I think that must have changed on another day. It was a day that my little sister, Joanne, was playing at their house.

It may have been the last day she played there.

On that day I learned why Claudia was so happy, because on that day she broke the code of silence.

On that day she crossed the border. She told my sister about Jesus.

It isn't that I had never heard His name. I am sure they talked about Him in the history books at school, but I never made any connection with His name and a normal person.

The only other time I heard His name was in my house when my father broke something or when my mother was overwhelmed. His name had no pleasant association.

The day that Claudia spoke about Jesus was different.

When Joanne came home, she flew into the house, bursting with excitement as one with news from afar.

"Mommy, mommy!" She threw open the door with excitement. Her little winter coat was unbuttoned as if she could not afford the time it took to button it with such important information to share.

"Mommy!" she cried. "Claudia said that we could know Jesus, too!"

Now, I do not know if it was a moment or an hour, but I do know that the temporary silence was cherished because I knew that it would not last. The only thing that I can compare that moment to was a classic *Abbott and Costello* episode. It was when Lou was in jail with some crazed man whose wife had deserted him on their honeymoon at Niagara Falls. He was perfectly sane and under control until someone mentioned Niagara Falls. Then he became undone.

My mother did not completely unravel, but the moment after she realized what my sister said, her countenance changed. Her attention was totally focused, and she spoke with clarity and in a commanding tone.

"I don't want to ever hear you say that name again! Do you hear me? He is not for us."

That was the end of the discussion and, so far as I remember, the last time I saw Claudia.

Some time later I wondered if they moved because of us.

No one ever talked about Jesus again while we grew up in that house. Oh, you might hear His name mentioned, but like Costello's Niagara Falls, it was never pleasant to hear.

What I did learn was that He'd died and that the Gentiles blamed us for killing Him.

That always puzzled me. If He was their God, how could the Jews be so tough that we could have killed Him?

Anyway, that was the last time I heard anything about Jesus. He certainly had no room for me, and I had no interest in Him.

How authentic a god could He be if He could not even defend Himself from a bunch of Jews, who were on the run from their enemies all throughout history?

Dismissed.

By the time I realized that I was shopping for authenticity—and by that I mean reality and purpose—I had already come to the subconscious conclusion that the Jewish perspective was not sufficient, nor was the Catholic or Protestant one. As far as I was concerned, the Western world was clueless as to the reason why I was here. With such a vacuum, I became open to a cyclone of philosophies that blew across my path.

I was not a pioneer, but I was an explorer.

The paths in front of me had already been trod; some were well paved, some had only sandal marks. During the late sixties, my friends and I wore our marks into the pavement. In fact, when it came time to leave for college, we made a pact that we would not go the bell-bottom, hippie route. We had concluded by then that drinking and chasing girls was satisfying enough. Smoking pot and dropping acid was for losers—guys who couldn't make it.

But by the time Christmas break came, all that had changed. Our pact completely dissolved.

My new path was the way of the sandals.

Love, peace, and happiness. Far out.

Very far out.

Fortunately, I survived the sixties and the seventies. Not all of my companions who followed that same path can say the same. The road of experience without restraint took a severe toll on my generation. Many who survived physically never recovered mentally.

When it comes to life, there is something to be said about making it up as you go along.

It simply does not work.

Instant gratification was the culture's driving philosophy. "If it feels good, do it." I needed more. Something deeper had to undergird why I did what I did. Rebellion against the norm was by itself completely negative.

Perhaps it was guilt. More than one Jewish boy could sense his mother's eyes looking over his shoulders through life, and no doubt that watchful feeling was part of my thinking, but for me it was a bit more. Without clearly identifying it at the time, I was looking for something else. I really wanted my life to be marked by something authentic.

The explorer in me wanted the discovery of finding that "something," and bringing it back to the land from which I set sail.

My journey began with the rejection of the world that I knew.

The Western hemisphere immersed in the Judeo-Christian heritage had left me flat.

I needed to head east. Since I had renounced the Protestant work ethic along with their religion, I had no money to travel across the sea. My journey would be through books and teachers who had already been there and, in my estimation, arrived.

My presupposition was that there was "someplace" at which I would arrive.

As I look back at my experience and the frail nature of simply making it through intact, I wish that there had been some ground rules to follow, even though I would have rejected them.

But here is where I would suggest to all future explorers my perspective: the exploration process is a legitimate phase of growing up. In fact, it is necessary.

For a belief system to be real and livable, it must have some historical consistency, recognizing that I am not the first person on the search for authenticity. The discovery has to include why the created world is so magnificent, yet life itself can be so hard. It has to explain the reason for the pain, the suffering and the longing for relief. It cannot ignore or dismiss this common human cry. Finally, the result has to leave us with a legitimate reason to hope. The discovery of the authentic will not simply end in bliss. It will be the beginning of a meaningful way of living here and now with the anticipation of a greater way ahead. For the life, which begins in this world, will be a shadow of the one to come in the next.

What I mean is this: at the end of this exploration, the process has to make sense. The outcome has to leave me in a "land" in which I cannot only survive, but also flourish, a place where I can sense that I belong, that I am vital and never lacking hope.

Without elaborating, personal experiences become a part of this journey of discovery. Whether it starts with the ocean or in the mountains, the desert, or the skies, we begin to discover the natural order of things. We recognize the cohesive nature of the properties of this world, whether we use our human eyes, a high-powered telescope, or an electron microscope. As far as the eye can see, there is farther to see in every direction. Is it endless, or does it just appear that way? Is it created or is it random? Is there any aim or purpose for it all? Or does it matter? So far the discovery has no answers, only observations.

In my quest for authenticity I needed to know about this place. I was not only an observer; I was a part of what is here, whether by chance or by design. When I took my first look around, I surmised that not everyone seemed to care about these matters.

Why did I?

Before I ever began an honest quest for authenticity, I had already drawn some conclusions. In synagogue I heard about the God of Abraham, Isaac, and Jacob—the God Who once was. In school I was taught about evolution and random chance. By the time I reached my senior year in high school in 1968, I began to consider the question posed on the cover of *Time Magazine*, "Is God Dead?" My answer was, "He must be," because I assumed most believed that He was dead—those that I knew lived as if as if there were no other reality. I subconsciously convinced myself that if that was what I believed, that is the way I should behave.

The natural conclusion was to live for *me*. I began a journey of self-intoxication. Whatever it took to experience more pleasure was reason enough to pursue it. Although that became my reality for a time, it intersected with another reality: the Vietnam War.

Not long after passing through the magical realm of this new culture, I was confronted with a paradox. If this world that I was helping to define was like the "never-ending party," then the

Vietnam War was like an older brother at the front door telling me it was time to come home and do my homework. Which one was true? How could I submit myself to both worlds? In one I was bound to no one, and in the other I was forced to constrain my pleasure by an immeasurable, unexplainable horror with which my own generation was grappling.

In the midst of my search I observed that a social conscience had begun to develop. My mind was collecting information that needed to be processed in order for me to find a valid conclusion. I was confused but unwilling to admit it. I needed greater understanding in order to explain the meaning of life.

Because something had gone wrong, awfully wrong.

Permit me to summarize what I now see was happening to me over a period of several years.

I wanted so much to enjoy my life. As I grew into adulthood, I tried so hard to believe that the possibility of enjoyment had to exist—not just on special occasions or when the good times rolled, but in moment-by-moment living. The problem for me was that I had no visible model to follow. Everyone that I had observed had an "oy veyism." Don't misunderstand: I saw many happy times and many happy faces, but they were always responsive. Whether it was a new car, job, or baby, the only things that made for happiness were external things. Sometimes, the external things were taken internally, like good food or drink, or in my era the advent of the "mind-altering psychedelics." Happiness on one day had no lasting effect. There was a default mechanism that returned to solemnity. It seemed that the longer a person lived, the more solemn he became. Perhaps that is why much of Jewish music is played with a mixture of major and minor chords. In this world, sorrow and joy are bedfellows. They co-mingle, and they are both legitimate.

I had a lot of questions.

For instance, why do I prefer to be happy rather than sad if both are legitimate?

Why do we spend money and time trying to become happy? Is it not possible simply to be happy?

The leading philosopher of my adolescence was Alfred E. Neuman. He was the voice of authority of *Mad Magazine*. His mantra to us was "don't worry, be happy."

Was happiness a real possibility or was it simply a state of mind that could be "willed" into position?

What I really needed at that point of my life was someone who could help me to validate my conundrum. I would have greatly benefited from someone who could have explained to me that I was confused. It was not because I was messed up or weird, but because I was looking for something to grasp that had no handles. I needed to learn that happiness was a wonderful human experience, but it was not a permanent one. What I needed was to learn how to be content, and I needed to learn that from someone who had arrived at that understanding.

I cannot honestly say that I was looking for that "someone," at least not then. I was more interested in the excitement of the discovery process. However, the more I discovered, the more I whittled away the prospect of finding someone who actually seemed to know and experience the meaning of contentment.

The surprise to me was that he would be from another generation and an an entirely different culture, but he would be the happiest man I would ever meet.

He was the Milkman.

CHAPTER 1

"It Must Be About Jesus"

*"For I have received of the Lord that which
also I delivered unto you…"*
1 Corinthians 11:23, ASV

When I first approached Pastor Al about the vision I had been given for writing this book, I expected resistance. In fact, a few people who knew him told me that he would never consent to it. Their reasoning was based on his humility. He never wanted to be the focus of attention. He recognized that his leadership would be a stumbling block if a person were to admire him rather than adore Jesus. There was no value in his "fame." People needed to know Jesus, not Al Isaksen. That was by holy design. He would not jeopardize that anticipated relationship at the altar of human charisma. He would rather be invisible.

There was too much at stake.

I should clarify something. When I say "vision," there were two parts to it: title and function. Both were very clear and came without effort. A picture, as they say, is "worth a thousand words." A few of those words have to do with "The Drop-off." First off it is straight forward— simply milk and maybe some bi-product. No instructions are necessary. Second is the release. As the metal case touches the cement stoop, it barely makes a sound. The milkman is careful with the product. It is too valuable, and it is intended to be there that morning. When he lets go of that case, he is like a pitcher on the mound. He has done it a thousand times. Every time that ball leaves his hand, it is meant to land in the catcher's mitt. When the last molecule of that ball is released from his fingers, he is no longer in control. The pitcher goes back to the mound, just as the milkman goes back to his truck.

He does not look for praise or admiration. His job is about the delivery. The pitcher is part of the team; the milkman is part of the company. It takes many players to bring the product to the table.

The message of the gospel of God in Jesus the Messiah is the very same way.

Pastor Al did not think that he should get any more recognition in the work of the gospel than anyone else. The glory of the operation belonged to Jesus. He was the head. Pastor Al would not risk the purposes of God for personal fame.

He understood that God was on the move. Not that He personally was moving, but that He was moving humanity, both individually and collectively, to a place and a purpose that was beyond this world, for it reached toward another dimension. He saw that place in the spirit, and it brought him great enthusiasm and determination. It also gave him a proper fear of God, fear that brings respect.

Pastor Al knew the gospel was not something he had invented. He was given revelation of "the salvation given to men" and a call to proclaim it for others to hear. He did not own it.

It was his job to properly deliver it. Whether it was carefully digested or spilled down the drain was not in his hands. What he was called to do was deliver it "in the same manner in which he also received it."

So when I told him about the book, he sounded a bit unsettled. The title is what initially troubled him. *The Milkman Story* sounded like a biography. Not unexpectedly, he was uncomfortable. When I told him that God had given me a vision for the book, the title, and even the cover picture, he needed time to consider.

A few weeks went by as doubts rolled through my mind.

Would he reject the idea of a book in honor of his life of service? Was this my concoction? Why would I even think that I could be involved in such a task? I had no experience at this level. Besides, those voices that rejected this project spoke the loudest in my ear. I felt the doubts crashing over me. Perhaps they were right. Who would want to read a book about him besides those who knew him? It might sell a few hundred copies at best—certainly a poor investment of time and effort and resources.

Having taken only a few steps out of the boat of comfort and onto the sea of expectancy, I began to doubt. I saw the contrary winds rolling my way, and I started to sink.

That is when a new voice arose over the waters, a still voice. It was the voice within. This voice spoke with a calmness and yet a confidence. It was the voice of the One Who is enthroned above the floods of doubt and insufficiency. It was the voice of calling, which tells me to be still and know that He is God. His whisper reminded me that I am to lean on His understanding, not my own, and that I am to call upon Him and He will show me great and mighty things that I have not known. As His child

I have received an anointing from above that I might do His will beneath. The good news of His kingdom was to be spread throughout the earth until He returned. Now it was my turn. I am a part of this generation who has received this liberating message, and it was now my part to play this role in this way. This was His design, not my own. My call was to do it and to know that I could do all things through Messiah Jesus, Who constantly infuses me with strength for the task.

Would I believe it and ride the doubts to shore, or would I allow their weight to drive me to the bottom and shipwreck?

I chose to believe.

A few days later I called Pastor Al. We chatted for a few minutes. His health was failing, and with each call I could sense his time on this earth fading. However, like every other conversation I have had with him in the twenty-seven years that I knew him, he turned my thoughts to Jesus.

"What is God speaking?" he would want to know.

I was not the only one he spoke to like that. He always put you on the spot, as if you were supposed to know. At the same time, he would never make you feel uncomfortable. It was his simple way of asking, "How's life with the Father? What have you been hearing lately?"

"How's the book coming?" he asked in a weak tone, but with such assurance and humility that I thought that God was listening in.

"Does that mean you are okay with it?" I asked sheepishly.

Pastor Al had told me previously that there was no value in a book about him. I had countered that I truly believed, and that by no means was I alone, that his calling was quite unique.

His simple life of visible faith in a manner that made him seem invisible was a message that needed to be proclaimed. It was a sermon in itself, and pastors throughout our country needed to hear it. What should be normal Christianity has been transformed into something foreign.

I listened as he spoke softly in a broken voice these words, which were undoubtedly drenched in his tears:

"It must be about Jesus."

CHAPTER 2

Pure Milk

"[A]s newborn babes, desire the pure milk
of the word, that you may grow thereby…"
1 Peter 2:2, NKJV

This book is about Jesus.

One of thousands.

I thought I should tell you in case that does not interest you.

I do not want to "milk" you of your attention. Jesus will have it another time, just not through this story. However, if Jesus does pique your interest, whether for the first time or since a long time ago, let me tell you what you are in for.

The Milkman Story is somewhat biographical, somewhat didactic, and somewhat apologetic. Since milk is used in the Bible as a metaphor for the Word of God, then a "milkman" can readily describe one who delivers the word. Al Isaksen is the Milkman in our story. He was an actual milkman when he met Jesus; he remained a milkman until Jesus called him to a higher route. "Pastor Al," as many knew him, was divinely prepared and groomed to serve a wide population of pilgrims, who settled on his "route" through the years. It is of no coincidence that the

Milkman Al became Pastor Al. His occupation and the nature of milk allow for many lessons to unfold.

Few would disagree that the American Church faces vast perils. Many in ministry encounter deep personal struggle as they attempt to faithfully serve their flock. Perhaps you are one. *The Milkman Story* is presented to bring fresh hope and inspiration through the simplicity of Pastor Al's ministry. His life is a lesson for you, the pastor who has been to seminary and mastered the doctrine, but whose experience totters between insecurity and pride. You long for an example to follow outside of your Bible's leather cover. Pastor Al is a pastor's pastor, and though he would shudder to hear this, his life in Christ should be required reading for any pastoral candidate.

Our last audience includes you who have had it with church. You have been there, done that. At one time you felt the longing to meet Jesus and follow Him, but you felt bitter disappointment in your church experience. You still like Jesus, but you have sworn off church.

Why is that?

I think there lies a clue in our present-day milk. You see, the cream has been skimmed off. Just go down the dairy aisle of any grocery store. So many containers say "milk," but which one is the real deal? At least they indicate what percentage of milk they actually have. In some way, I wish that church buildings would display similar honesty. Beneath their church sign that invites you in should be another clearly marked space letting us know what is inside:

- 2% Jesus
- 1% Jesus
- Skim Jesus

The truth is that Jesus said, "I will build My church." In far too many of these places, the Carpenter has never even driven a nail.

There still is, however, a remnant. Where Pastor Al served, Jesus was at work, and the people participated joyfully. Why was that?

It was because the milkman delivered the product. He did not first reinvent it.

Jesus was "the Builder," and Pastor Al was wise enough to let Him build. He displayed the courage to trust Jesus at His word. When an individual came into fellowship at Gospel Community Church, that person was considered to be a hand-picked stone by the Almighty God. He was designed with a specific purpose and would be shaped for a unique place in the "church" that Jesus was building. On either side of this new "member," as well as beneath him and upon him, would be other integral stones, each vital parts of this living structure. Pastor Al saw this as a sacred process. His place was to deliver the word, or the "milk," that would strengthen the individual and fortify his position in God's building, like mortar does with brick. (I find it interesting that some masons call mortar "milk.")

What set Pastor Al apart was his delivery. Because the "word" is alive and the "stones" are alive, so the message had to be alive, and thus the "building" was alive. In Al Isaksen, that word was lived out. Whenever you were with him, you experienced the nourishment that whole milk offers. It not only brought strength, it built character. Our story is about that common thread. The benefit of pure milk is widespread and historical. Those who continually drink from its source join the stream of history. They become the people who positively affect their surroundings. Pastor Al is one "milkman" who had faithfully delivered the message once delivered to him, so that others to follow would continue to do the same.

Al Isaksen ran that race, and he crossed the finish line. He spent his last days in bed at his simple yet comfortable trailer home in central Florida. Like the apostle Paul, he was a "house prisoner" in his final days. People would come and visit him from all over. Most of us were those who experienced his loyal love and outpoured life. He held nothing back to the very end. His physical heart steadily shut down, threatening daily to abandon its post, yet his spiritual heart remained strong in God. He waited expectantly for his last heartbeat, when he would awaken in the presence of Jesus. His deepest regret was leaving his precious wife, Dorothy. They had been "one" for over sixty years. He knew, though, that their separation would be brief. His sorrow was more for the state of the Church.

Pastor Al would have never agreed to the writing of this book except for one reason. The purpose of this book, I promised him, was that someone's heart would be so ignited through his example that a living active faith would come alive. Perhaps as you read on, you will drink from his source and become that one.

And I will have kept my promise.

CHAPTER 3

Milk Power

*"And even when [I am] old and gray, O
God, do not forsake me, / Until I declare
Your strength to [this] generation, / Your
power to all who are to come"*

Psalm 71:18, NAS

Today in America there is a quest for strength and power.

I am not talking about politicians; they have always sought for more control and attention. I am better acquainted with the average Joe or Jane.

I began to recognize this phenomenon when I considered the drinks offered in the deli cooler. Have you noticed the titles?

Powerade®, 5-hour ENERGY®, Red Bull®, Jolt®...

I get the impression that we need something to combat our weakness, and lo and behold the marketplace has provided redemption—or distraction! At least they have identified our need. We feel zapped. We are a tired people, and we want to wake up. Our bodies are calling for help. We find ourselves in a place where we just don't seem to have what it takes to meet the task at hand or to compete with the other guy.

It must be that I need a drink.

If we turn on the tube or open our magazine of choice, we can always find someone with a drink in hand—a power drink. A second look tells us that this is a woman with determination. Not only has she resolve, but she knows what she wants and where to get it. And the gentleman, not only does he have a "six pack," but he grips that can with such great strength and gulps down so much power that we know he will crush that can in the palm of his hand as soon as he finishes it. Then, we can be assured, he will slam that ball, vault that bar, or win that race. He will be left satisfied and accomplished.

Just what is missing in our lives? Where can I get a case of that stuff? "Power" has sales attraction because it is a common human need. We cannot survive without it. Even if we could manufacture a source of power, we would need a source to do so. We are powerless without that "source." We need to look outside of ourselves.

There is a verse in Psalms that says, "Power belongs to God."

An interesting attribute about this God is that He, the source and distributor of all power, is humble. He is not self-attracting. In fact, He is so humble that He is invisible. It isn't that He wants to be alone. On the contrary, He continually invites us to come unto Him. That is what He says, but often He aids the process through our physical needs. He is very subtle in His approach for friendship.

I like this verse as well:

"[M]y God will supply all your needs according to His riches in glory in Christ Jesus" (Philippians 4:19, NAS).

Most people interpret this by saying that when I am hungry, God shall supply my food. When I am thirsty He gives me drink.

When I am weak, He gives me strength. There is undoubtedly an element of truth to this equation, but I have come to see it from a different perspective.

We are complex beings. Everyone agrees on that. Christians and atheists share the same basic needs. The Christian may state that God takes care of his needs, and the unbeliever may say that he takes care of himself. My issue isn't with the satisfaction of the need, such as water for thirst, but with the need itself.

Why am I thirsty in the first place? Why hungry? Why tired? Why weak? It is common to man. Not only that, but our needs don't always show up on schedule. Nor do they all appear at once. When they do come, they insist upon all of our attention and won't stop nagging until they are satisfied.

To my understanding, God has never openly declared that He has made our needs, but He has confessed to the fact that He has made us. If He is that capable, He could have made our lungs to operate within a closed system. They would not be left gasping for air if deprived of oxygen for a couple of minutes. He could have designed stomachs that know nothing of the concept of hunger.

So we have needs. Most often, things from outside of the body satisfy those needs. We need to go somewhere for satisfaction, every time.

If we think of God as merely being the One Who "supplies the supply" and not the "need," we end up with a religion.

I don't like religion. I am not alone. Jesus despised religion.

It is an artificial approach to fill an inner need. Like Red Bull® is to real power, religion is to a relationship with Jesus. Each religion seems to attract people with similar perspectives. As time passes, they design some sort of cathedral around themselves where they sense their need is being satisfied. Whether it is through preaching or penance, the parishioners feel some need within being met. But it does not last.

"But my God will supply all your needs according to His riches in glory in Christ Jesus."

Notice that the verse ends with the almost parenthetical phrase "in Christ Jesus." This means that the "need" and then the "supply" are all wrapped in Jesus. The need is no longer being supplied from outside the body but from the Spirit of Jesus within. God supplies the "need for the need." Instead of making us as self-sufficient beings, He created us as needy people. His purpose is for us to see that *He* is actually our greatest need.

We are designed to be in relationship with the One Who made us. Religion is a man-made attempt to meet the spiritual needs of men. It can no better do that to the spiritual man than 5-Hour Energy® can do with a tired body in need of nutrition and rest. For too long America has lived without true spiritual life, which is ultimately and only found in Christ, the Messiah.

Forgive us, Lord, for our pitiful attempts to replace the pure gospel with artificially colored and flavored water. We have exchanged Your "Milk" for Kool-Aid, and we are sick and empty.

Milk is a need.

You may not consider that to be true now, but it once was. By design, our bodies needed what only milk could provide. A mother's anatomy was engineered to provide milk for her newborn baby. By the time 1950 rolled around, the marketplace aided by chemistry came up with its own idea to provide a new source, but for millennia the human race survived by original design. What they came up with was a man-made product and package, but it was still milk. The source was changed, but the need remained the same. It always does.

Here is where we must take a look at another dimension.

We live in three dimensions and we travel in a fourth: time.

There is another dimension of ours, though it is often ignored, and that is the spiritual. We are spiritual beings. In fact we are spirit; we live in a body, and we possess a soul.

When the Bible gives illustrations, as when Jesus taught in parables, they are spiritual lessons using earthly or physical objects.

Milk is one of them.

It is used to depict the gospel message.

When we think of milk, our minds paint a picture based upon our experience with it. Most of us, but certainly not all, can call to mind a soothing and energetic moment. That cool glass of milk brought a sense of well-being, of expectation, of a new day unfolding. It left us refreshed and satisfied.

But others would say, "No way!"

"Milk is disgusting!"

Unfortunately, that response is equally valid and must be taken into account if we are to have a discussion centered on milk. Good or bad, milk is the illustration that God used to describe the gospel. *Gospel* literally means "good news."

Good news is not initially good for every hearer. For instance, the headline that reads "Bank Robber Caught, Thrown in Jail" is good news for the bank, but not for the robber. It may *become* good news to him, but that depends on his response to his new condition: captured.

So it is with the gospel.

"Good news, the kingdom of God is at hand" is not very good news to the one who is quite satisfied with his status quo. "Life is good, thank you, and I am quite capable of taking care of myself. Besides, I never was a fan of milk."

As valid as milk is to illustrate a baby's need for his mother's milk, it is still not a perfect illustration to describe the gospel. Nor is there another.

That is because any attempt to perfectly illustrate spiritual truth with physical objects will fall short. How can we translate from one dimension to another without knowing the new language?

At one point Jesus said, "I am the Door."

What He was saying is that He is the way from this dimension to the next.

Now, if my fingers had been slammed in a car door when I was little, I might be hesitant to go much further with His illustration. However, if I am willing to trust the nature of the teacher, I can proceed with His lesson.

We must become willing to be tutored by the Translator, or we will remain outside the realm of understanding.

Milk is a great illustration for a source of strength and power.

It contains at least nine essential nutrients. Cell growth, muscle mass, and bone development derive much of their help from milk. It helps to regulate the nervous system and produces energy. Potassium, which is crucial in the regulation of the balance of body fluids, is found ten times more in milk than in an equal serving of the leading sports drink.

Our next step is to take this common knowledge of the physical world, with us into a lesson about the spiritual world. Though the spiritual world is unseen, it is not unsuspected.

Because man is a spiritual being, he spends time and energy in search of his spiritual identity. On this journey, each of us travels in seemingly different directions. This is largely due to our upbringing. As much as the choice to be raised on mother's milk or goat's milk is not ours, so it is with our exposure to a spiritual life. The vast majority of American parents in the last several decades have said "not interested." Some may opt for a dose of religion, but that is man-made and not spiritual in nature. As a result, the children grow through adolescence into adulthood and continue to live void of spiritual life.

I should say that at our present level of conversation "spiritual life" is neither positive nor negative. It is neither good nor bad. However, because we are spiritual by nature, we will take roads that will determine where we ultimately land. In the one we discover spiritual life, and in any other, spiritual death.

One is the "way"; the others are a dead end.

The gospel "milk" is an invitation to experience spiritual life in its fullest sense.

It is the product that the Milkman delivered. As a result, the atmosphere surrounding his ministry was filled with spiritual life and power. It spilled out into the streets and into the nations. It was the most effective way of delivering the product. He was not the product, nor did he produce it. But he was a faithful deliverer, a Milkman in the truest sense.

CHAPTER 4

"...and you know it don't come easy"

"Good News"

In 1957, it was not good news to me that my parents were planning to buy a new house. Our first move from Brooklyn was to a little ranch house in Syosset, New York. This house would no longer fit our expanding family, so we were moving to the "country." They had bought a new one a little farther east on Long Island, on a quarter-acre lot, which was once part of a potato farm that was now growing houses. Brooklyn and my earliest memories and attachments were fading in the west, and I was a bit unsettled.

I did like all the dirt that surrounded our new house, and I knew that I would still be with my family, but what about Joey Moliterno and Johnny Amols? They were my people, and I felt crushed that they would be so no more. My parents said that I would have new neighbors and make new friends, but I wasn't so sure. I didn't see any new kids on the street. In fact, there was no street. How was a boy supposed to play ball on dirt?

And what about Mrs. Goeltzer? Wouldn't she miss me? She was my third-grade teacher. She knew me. I was not sure that she liked me, but I was in her class, and I sat at my own desk.

Soon I would go to a new school and sit at another desk. I really did not want a new teacher. I was pretty sure that she would not like me. I wished that I had the power to convince my parents that this was a bad idea.

That was before the chocolate milk arrived.

Once the new house was up, we would pile into our 1952 Nash Rambler and drive through the suburbs of Nassau County into the unchartered wilderness of Huntington Station, Long Island. I had never seen so much land before. It seemed barren and uninviting. Little did I know that those spaces would fill in with houses and roads, shopping centers and parking lots. The potatoes that once grew plentifully from the fertile ground would soon disappear. In their place would be row after row of houses. Like the potatoes, each row would have the appearance of the one beside it. It would take a few decades before the trees would grow full enough around the houses to bring identity and a sense of belonging for the houses they shaded.

Within each house a family would grow. Young men, many of whom had spent their strongest years defending the world from the rise of ruthless tyranny, would settle here.

Out of the boroughs of New York City they would venture as the last of the American pioneers with their wives, children, and in many cases, second-hand furniture.

They did not come in covered wagons, nor did they battle ravaging diseases and wild Indians like the pioneers from yesteryear. Nevertheless, family life in the suburbs would not be without great challenge.

My parents in many ways were settling there for the same reason as their neighbors. The city was becoming overcrowded and more dangerous. Many of these pioneers were second-generation immigrants, who grew up in apartments on city streets with a father who barely scraped together enough income for food, clothing, and rent. The hope of parents like mine was to provide the opportunity for their children to go further in life than they had. It was part two of the American dream. To me it was a nightmare.

That all changed when the milkman arrived.

I can still see his black shoes, shining brightly against his white-cuffed pants. He stood there patiently in what would one day be our kitchen, waiting for my parents to finish talking to another strange man. The man with the white pants and black shoes also had a white hat. He smiled at me and seemed to like me, even though I didn't smile back. He was a stranger and we never talked to them. I leaned against my father's leg until my parents were done with the other stranger. The milkman introduced himself, and shook hands with my father. He asked my mother if it would be okay if he could give me something. Apparently she said yes, because the next thing I remember was him handing me a bottle of chocolate milk. The rest was a blur. I had never tasted chocolate milk from a bottle, let alone my own bottle. He called it a sample. I called it life-changing. Boredom immediately vanished from my day.

Don't misunderstand me; we had chocolate milk in our house. Every Jewish family did. It was staple food. We actually made our own. It wasn't like the Mennonites making apple butter, but we did pump our own chocolate syrup from gallon bottles. My uncle Lou provided them. Uncle Lou was married to my Aunt Frieda. He weighed about four hundred pounds and always wore a jacket and tie. He sat on the same chair whenever we visited them in their apartment in Far Rockaway. I cannot ever remember him standing up. He sat there smoking a long cigar. He did not say much, but when he did, everyone stopped talking. At some point in the day he would call my name in an indistinguishable, gruff voice that rolled out of his hugeness:

"Paully."

I would immediately stop what I was doing and go over to him. He would then pull out a roll of bills and hand me one. He did that with all the cousins. At the end of the visit he would tell my father, Allie, to remember the bottle of syrup. It was in the trunk of his '57 Caddy. It was not ordinary syrup; it came from his candy store. They used it to make chocolate egg creams, which they sold to the customers who would sit on round, shiny swivel seats against the linoleum counter. I loved my uncle Lou, although he rarely spoke to me. I later learned that his candy shop was a front for his business as a bookie, and that he was a former getaway driver for Murder Incorporated, the Jewish version of the Italian Mafia. I still loved him, though. It's funny how chocolate milk could produce such a strong bond.

Back to our new house, chocolate milk unleashed its power again. For the first time I can remember, I talked to a stranger. It was forbidden. He was not family, he was not a known neighbor or a friend of my parents. He was not even Jewish. I don't know how I knew that, but I did. The gift of chocolate milk made two new things happen. First, I felt that moving to a new house may have some advantages and, second, that strange men may not all be as dangerous as I suspected.

This is where some very brief Jewish history needs to enter the story.

My parents come from immigrant families in Eastern Europe. My mother's side of the family was from Poland, and my father was from Russia. Their Jewish families lived in secluded ghettos, or, in Yiddish, *shtetls*. Ghettos were portions of a city that secluded a certain minority population. In Jewish history it was a way of controlling their activity and a way to dehumanize them in the eyes of the larger population. Eventually it made it easier to perform mass murder on them. Over the centuries of Jewish persecution, Jews for the most part were forced to live together, separated from the rest of the population, which was made up of Gentiles. The Jews were accused of many social evils wherever they went. Manipulating money, initiating plagues, using Gentile children's blood for their Passover rites—these were just a few of the accusations. Though they have no valid basis, they were accepted as truth and passed down from generation to generation. It was only a matter of time before the Jews would arise and wreak havoc, they expected, so they needed to be huddled together or evicted until a "Final Solution" was discovered. That is why Hitler's plan was so smoothly executed. It had very little opposition among the Gentile nations. The Jewish voice had no advocacy, no influence, and hence, no protection. This anti-Semitic culture of enmity reached new heights with the rise of Hitler in the 1930s.

Jewish immigration had experienced a dramatic rise in America in the previous decades. Almost the entire population of Jewish immigrants came through the ports of New York. In comparison to the fear of annihilation that loomed in Europe, America seemed like a safe haven. It did become a haven, but the ancient suspicion and enmity awaited them— or should I say "us."

Most American Jews still live in the surrounding New York metropolitan community. Today, very few have any idea of what took place in that area when their parents and grandparents began to settle in this new land of opportunity and tolerance. That is because their parents did not discuss anti-Semitism, and American history class did not teach it. However, its ugly wheels almost spun out of control in 1939.

In February of that year, the German American Bund, which was in close cooperation with the "Christian Front," rallied in front of Madison Square Garden to proclaim the rights of white Gentiles, the "true patriots." President FDR, whom they considered a friend of the Jews, was giving a speech inside the Garden. A small group inside consistently booed him, while outside the crowd of 20,000 chanted, "Heil Hitler."

During the same time period, this pro-Nazi movement gained momentum all across America, but it reached its height in New York and New Jersey. Long Island was their central gathering site each summer, where so-called youth camps were held in the town of Yaphank. It became clear that their intention was not a gathering where the kids would be singing "Kumbayah" around the campfire. In August of 1938, *The New York Times* reported that the Long Island railroad filled its cars with the greater portion of the 40,000 who attended their largest pro-Nazi rally. When they entered the camp, they would parade down the main avenue, which they named Adolph Hitler Street.

The German American Bund was dissolved when the United States entered WWII. Sadly, its spirit did not.

Though few Long Islanders today are familiar with their history, it was current events for my folks, and their decision to move farther east on the island would bring them closer to the place that Hitler eyed as a potential destination once Europe was under his full control.

This was why my parents were suspicious of the Gentile community to which we were migrating. Though I was never told why, I knew that I was forbidden to talk with strange men. Innately, I knew that meant Gentile men.

So when that milkman handed me a bottle of chocolate milk along with his gentle smile, it dismantled a centuries-old barricade, called Gentile distrust, for a Jewish child like me. Somehow in my mind, a new possibility was opened to me. Perhaps some of them do like us, and maybe we can become part of their world. Could it be that what they have to offer is worth exploring? I know my little mind did not think in diplomatic wavelengths, but I believe that bottle of chocolate milk, which a kind man from a foreign culture offered, opened a door for me to explore his world and its message.

It is worth noting again that this Gentile stranger was a milkman.

CHAPTER 5

Not Relevant

If it doesn't pertain to me, I'm not interested.

Milk can fit into that category. Its usefulness can be swept away with childhood.

So can the gospel.

It is for Sunday school kids or old folks.

The little kids need some wholesome storybook tales that keep them occupied while their parents are fulfilling their religious obligations upstairs amidst the stained-glass sanctuary. The elderly need it to ease the uncertainty of their latter days. For the rest of us, we have enough going on dealing with issues of real life, thank you.

Not only are we through with milk, the gospel has lost its relevance to reality.

Allow me to put this in the context of my upbringing. I grew up in the 1950s and 1960s. When my family moved to Long Island, we became part of the minority. In Brooklyn, the Jewish neighborhoods were not very different than they had been in Eastern Europe, in the sense that Jews lived together. It was not by political mandate as it had been across the pond, but for the sake of preservation and security. As their families grew and the apartment space shrunk, many of the young married couples set their eyes to the east, on the rising of the new suburban hope. A vast land was being developed that offered fresh air, job opportunities, and new schools.

The greatest snag for the Jewish young pioneers was that there were no real neighborhoods. Houses were going up fast—real fast—but they were going up one at a time. My parents could choose their house but not their neighbors. Jews moving east might have other Jewish families in their development, but the chances of living close to each other were quite slim. They would be moving into a Gentile world, with Protestant and Catholic churches in place. I am not sure how they got to know each other and form associations, but they did, and very slowly, they began to gather in storefront synagogues until their "temple" could be constructed.

Even though there was a sense of hopefulness about their new roots, the reality of White European history loomed in the recent darkness. How the Jewish family would fit in was a story yet to unfold in modern American history.

We had very few Jewish neighbors close by, but somehow I knew each house inhabited by Jews. I had even fewer Jewish friends that I hung out with as I approached high school. Even though I witnessed Nazi signs and sayings, scratched into the cubicles of public restrooms, which debased the Jews, I personally did not experience direct anti-Semitic slurs until high school. Perhaps I was sheltered, or maybe I just did not look like the stereotype image, but as my social sphere grew to include more Gentiles from many backgrounds, things changed. I discovered that Jews were frequently considered a separate class of people. We were accused of the murder of Jesus. He was the federal head of their religions, and we did not believe in the New Testament or the gospel. It seemed to me that there was a bit of secrecy, because no one ever told me about Jesus, nor did anyone seem to know anything about this gospel.

One thing that seemed to be without argument was that the Jews were different, and one needed to be suspicious of "us."

It was a rare Jewish boy in my generation who played in the Little League or joined the Boy Scouts. If I had been asked, I would have done both, but I knew it was not for me, even though I was never told why. It was implied that they were Gentile gatherings. Besides, we had Hebrew school to attend.

I followed my parents' lead: I was cautious but not worried. In fact, by the time I was a senior in high school, I felt confident that I had proved myself to be as much a Gentile as my "goyim" friends were; I could carry on and cause trouble with the best of them. In fact, I considered myself to be one of their kind.

That is until we would drink, and I am not talking about, milk. Perhaps it was a false sense of courage, or a latent troubling attachment to the historical account of my ancient people, but when I heard a Jewish slur in conversation, whether in a bar or a diner, my anger would flare. Occasionally it would lead to a physical fight, which in those days would lead to a brawl. This trail of anger followed me into my college days as well as my early-married life. The only interruption seemed to be the love and peace movement of my hippie years, which appeared on the scene as a level playing field for people of all backgrounds.

It was not until I met the Milkman that I actually heard the gospel.

Strangely, I had already heard that Jesus was God and that He loved me and that He wanted to meet me. If I were willing, He would become my Messiah, or as the Gentiles put it, my Savior. I will never forget the day when that became a reality. I gave my life to Him on the same day that I was so close to killing my Jew-hating, Hungarian-Communist boss with a shovel...but that is another story.

My relationship with Jesus began with my yearlong reading of the Bible and my confrontation with the claims of Jesus, which were in front of me. I could ignore my need no longer, and my lifelong quest for meaning was met on my kitchen floor in the spring of 1979. I still had never heard the gospel preached, though, until I heard it from Pastor Al when we attended his church.

Once I heard it, I was hooked. As I began meeting fellow believers, it was like meeting my long-lost family. They loved and accepted me, even though they knew that I was a Jew. I made that clear from the beginning. What was strange was that, for the first time in my life, I was told that being Jewish made me special. I was not sure about being special, but I was certain it was rare. It would not be long before I met a few Jewish believers, but for now I felt safe and honored even though I was still different, actually even more different than before.

I needed to tell someone. My atheist father was first on my list. I thought for sure that he would hear me. There was no one I wanted to hear the good news more than him. I was certain he would be equally excited and responsive.

I couldn't have been more wrong.

"If you scratch them deep enough," he said, "they will bleed anti-Semitism," as if completely disinterested.

"Dad, these people are different. The Gentiles that you have met were not the same," I insisted. "These are true Christians. The ones you know and the ones who claimed to be Christians in history were frauds."

It was a hard sell, and it would continue to be for three decades of sharing the gospel with him. He had heard and seen too much. The message of hatred and hypocrisy, which he knew intimately, spoke louder than my new "fad." If he were to hear me out, the message would have to be relevant and my faith authentic.

"You wait and you'll see. This pastor of yours is out for money, and he doesn't care whose pocket it comes from."

I was out to prove him wrong and, in so doing, prove the gospel true. I had given my life to the Jewish Messiah and had no intentions of taking it back.

CHAPTER 6

Clean Cup

M ilk is matter, and the gospel is a message.

Both have life-giving potential, but they operate at different levels in the human experience. Milk is intended for bodily growth and development, while the gospel is intended for spiritual life and discipline.

Milk, as we know it, has affected our growth physically. Because it is a substance, it has physical properties that attract us at some physical level. It might begin with our eyes. A baby sees a bottle and begins to reach for it. If he cannot reach it, he begins to cry. At this point, the physical relationship with the product becomes emotional. It reaches the level of the soul.

One baby reaches for the bottle, another rejects it.

For one there is a thirst, for the other, distaste.

I can remember a time when milk became repulsive to me.

Our suburban street was the first one in our sub-division. The developers had the foresight to throw in a sycamore tree in front of each house, trees which have since grown up to provide a good bit of shade and privacy, as well as a home for the birds and squirrels. But back then they were mere twigs that would bend over if a bird landed on them.

There were no fences to separate the homes at that time—though now there are miles of them—so neighbors got to know each other. You had no place to hide.

Maybe that is what made my life adventurous. I could travel from my house to another through the backyards along the tiny bushes that marked the property edges. To me it was wide-open frontier. Occasionally, we would have to run between the houses to get to the street, and then run across the street and someone's front lawn to return to our backyard highway. It was dangerous at times because some neighbors didn't want you that close, and they would let you know it if they spotted you.

Mean old Mr. Martin was one of them. If a rubber ball landed on his front lawn it was like a hand grenade about to explode. A pink Spaulding ball was a precious commodity in those days; not everyone owned one. We would dive on the street to stop it from going down a sewer drain and vanishing forever. But landing on Mr. Martin's lawn was a different story.

He actually had a lawn.

Everyone had grass, at least small patches of it between the dirt, but he actually had a lawn. I don't know if he peeked from behind his curtains to watch his grass grow or to simply wait for an intruding child, who would foolishly attempt to walk on it. To my knowledge he never physically apprehended anyone, but we all cringed in fear when his door would fly open and his wrath poured out like flames.

So there was danger in our neighborhood, a place only the fast and fearless would dare to tread.

However, that was not like the house next door to Mr. Martin.

Diagonally across the street from my family's house lived the Reynolds. They had two boys, and in those days we spent many

Saturday mornings together, playing ball or letting our imaginations run loose to become soldiers or cowboys. Mrs. Reynolds was always smiling, as was Mr. Reynolds, but he always seemed like he was in the middle of a thought. He was either a publisher or an editor; I'm not sure, nor did I know the difference. I did know they had books all over the place, and many of them lay open in different piles and at different angles. At other houses the books were all on the shelf, except for one on the end table next to the lamp. I wasn't attracted to books then, but Mr. Reynolds certainly was. Judging by his thick glasses, he must have spent most of his time reading.

Maybe that is why he didn't see the egg.

One Saturday morning, his boys and I were playing in their yard, and we came into their house all hot and sweaty. Mrs. Reynolds figured that we must be in need of hydration, so with a smile she said to her husband, "Bob, give the boys a glass of milk. They look very thirsty."

Little did I know that my entire life was about to change.

Mr. Reynolds was standing at the kitchen sink washing the breakfast dishes. This time, his thick black glasses were slid down upon the edge of his nose. Perhaps that is why he did not notice that what he was about to do would keep me from ever returning to his house.

"Sure, dear," he answered.

And with a partial smile that was still entertaining a much deeper thought than the task in front of him, he grabbed a glass and began to pour me some milk from the container on the table.

Mrs. Reynolds was a thoughtful woman. She knew that I was thirsty and that I was taught to be polite and would never ask for a drink. I was quite thankful that she was my neighbor.

In the next moment I would not be so sure.

As I reached for the glass, the glass that I expected to simultaneously quench my thirst and still my hunger, would do neither. In fact, my relationship with milk and with the Reynolds household would never again be the same.

For as I reached for the glass and then held it in my hand, I realized that there was something terribly wrong. Before my very eyes was a sight that no child should ever have to endure. I suddenly faced a predicament that my young mind could have never expected—a decision before me that I was not prepared to make.

There was egg on the glass.

Maybe he didn't realize it or perhaps it was their practice, but that glass had not been washed since breakfast.

In my vast memory I had never drunk from a glass at home that had egg on it.

But this was even worse. It had someone else's egg on it.

I felt as if I were standing there for days not knowing what to do. Should I say something about the egg, should I refuse to drink it, should I pretend, or should I just get as sick on the outside as I felt on the inside? I had no instruction of how to behave in this situation. All that I knew was to say "thank you" or "no, thank you," and that was already settled. There was no turning back, or I would violate the laws of politeness that had been etched within me. It didn't help matters that my friend had already gulped his milk down and stared at me, wondering what was taking me so long.

So I did it.

I took a drink, and it was worse than I thought. Not only was the milk disgusting, it was lukewarm. I put the glass down on the counter and ran outside. As the screen door creaked behind me, I made up my mind to never pass through it again.

Although there was a clear contrast in the behavior of our two Gentile neighbors across the street, that day they became as one, both to be avoided.

Milk became a curse to me that day, and I resisted it whenever I could.

I have met people who feel the same way about the gospel.

All you have to do is mention it and they cringe. They don't want to hear about it.

Perhaps you are one of them. At one point, the message sounded good and right and even appealing. Like most newborn babes, you desired more for a time, and then your appetite changed. Was it the milk that soured, or was it the way it was delivered to you? Did your glass have egg on it?

Recently I hired a young man to work for me. He was a good friend of my son. We got to talk about things that mattered, and the topic turned to church. Even though he continues to go to church, he does so mainly so his mother doesn't have to go by herself. He seemed eager to give his assessment of the condition of the church, which I was eager to hear. What could be more important to hear than an emerging adult's perspective of the "institution" that should be the most powerful one in shaping our nation's future?

His assessment was not very assuring. He told me that the pastor was the story. He ran the church and the service. He greeted the people, made the announcements, and prayed the prayers. When it was time to leave, he stood at the door with a big smile and bade his people a blessed week, until one day some neighborhood kids were spotted riding their bikes in the parking lot and then across the lawn. At this point the story became more defining. What was a normally scheduled moment of Norman Rockwell serenity suddenly became a red-flushed response to some young boys being young boys. Perhaps they thoughtlessly rode their bikes on the front lawn like little boys are prone to do, not thinking that the front of a church was not a safe place to be. Apparently, it was not—at least not on a Sunday morning, not in front of this church. I suppose it was not much different than Mr. Martin's front lawn.

The pastor seemed to forget where he was, whom he was greeting, and even worse—far worse—Whom he represented. His attention turned to the boys and the disruption they had caused to his routine. As my son's friend continued the story, his face distorted. He was repelled by what he witnessed as the pastor publicly chastised those bike-riding infidels.

"How will any of them want to come to church or worship God if that is how the pastor acts?" He looked at me for an answer.

I wished at that moment that I was shocked and appalled, but I was not.

I had heard the story before. It wasn't the same church or the same pastor. Nor was it the front lawn of the church building. It was the egg-on-the-glass story, and it was still repulsive.

I have wondered at times how fragile this gospel message is. It is a good message. In fact, it is a great message, but delivery is everything. Even a thirsty man would not care to drink sour milk, nor would he want to drink fresh milk from a glass with the morning eggs stuck to its side.

"You hypocrites!" Jesus told the religious leaders of His day. "You clean the outside of the cup and dish, but inside they are full of greed and self-indulgence."

Allow me to spiritualize for a moment.

The Bible describes people in many illustrative ways. One of those descriptions is as "vessels." We are containers. That is one of the ways that God sees us. When He looks at us, He looks beyond and within. He sees us as mortal, yet spiritual beings made in His image.

God is the Creator of all things. The very last thing that He created was humankind. When He was finished with all that He made, His assessment was that it was all very good. The implication of this statement is beyond profundity because we know now that all is not good. Back then, though, the God of the universe had two vessels with whom He could enjoy close companionship on a continual basis. It was a fellowship of love and trust like no other. Into those two lives He poured vast amounts of wisdom and knowledge and understanding. They were vessels that sparkled with radiance of joy and contentment. Into their lives flowed reservoirs of spiritual life that converted to meaningful, maximized human potential.

Until they were tempted.

I would like to explore this event, but for now let's just consider what happened to them as vessels.

They began to crack.

Not only did they let out what was once sacred, they began to let in that for which they were not designed. As time went on, the cracks did not heal, nor could they. They were passed down to the next generation, and with each succeeding one, the cracks enlarged. The containers, which were designed for great eternal purposes, had become hard to distinguish from the animal kingdom they were called to subdue.

Milk can be a wonderful, nutritious drink, but if the container is dirty, it has lost all its appeal.

What if God sees us spiritually and morally as containers? What if He sees our inside as clearly as we view each other's dress?

How many pastors and church leaders have walked into immoral relationships and continued to preach a message of purity?

Stepping up to the pulpit with gravity and seeming conviction, standing at the door when they finish, smiling warmly at their congregants as they bid them peace, knowing all along that their cup is not clean on the inside.

Pastor Al was a good milkman. He knew the importance of the product and how the customer valued its freshness.

That is how it was with the gospel. He delivered it from a clean cup and it tasted fresh.

His love for the Bible came out of his love for Jesus. He had an acute understanding of the spiritual needs of the congregation. It was wrapped up in knowing Jesus. Pastor Al knew that his knowledge of the Bible was not the issue, nor was it his ability to communicate it. Though he was well read, it was the Lord Who was the source of his message, not a library. He preached out of intimacy as if he were in the middle of conversation with his Maker when we all walked in.

Years later when I began to preach, I wrestled over a message. I thought of Pastor Al and how at rest he appeared as opposed to how anxious I was feeling. It was then that the still small voice of the Spirit spoke to me: "You do not prepare the message, the message prepares you."

CHAPTER 7

In the Beginning

Most of us have a problem with God.

Because He is viewed as the Supreme authority, we associate Him with the role of a disciplinarian. Like the principal or the policeman, He is coming to get us as soon as we mess up. If that were all He was about, He would be worth avoiding at all cost.

That is precisely why the truth is so important. It breaks the power and the bondage of deception. Deception is like the air that we breathe. We don't notice it. For years we grow up developing an image of "God" that unknowingly shapes our behavior. At some point we each determine whether we will explore if He is real or not before we even decide to trust Him. Like the air, we get our information about God from every direction. It blows in and out of our lives. By the time we reach adolescence, we have decided how much distance we will allow between God and ourselves, or whichever "higher power" we may reference.

The Bible, though, is very clear about God. Not only does the story of creation begin with Him, it is the story of God. He was "there" even before it began. He has been "there" ever since, and He will be "there" at the end of the ages. The Bible is also the story of man. However, man enters a story that is already in progress. Upon his arrival, the man is introduced to

God as a willing companion. The story continues as God reveals Himself as man's Maker, his Father, and his potential Friend.

It is the story of relationship: God continually inviting man into a joint venture with Himself.

There is a problem, though. God is Spirit.

Man is given a spirit, but he lives in a physical world evidenced by the senses. Although he is invited, man must choose to explore God. That does not mean that man is to ignore what is physical in nature; but he is not to become so attached to it that he is blinded by the temporal nature of physical things.

The created world helps him in the process because every facet of it is so incredible. From the DNA of a flea to the star-filled night sky, there is the cry of the created to consider its Creator. Every system of the created world is capable of leaving us in awe of its endless splendor. Whether it encompasses the sense of sight, sound, smell, touch, or taste, the study of any aspect of any living system will take countless lifetimes to explore. Yet the endless nature of created things only leads us to paradox. It appears eternal, but it is not. Though the full understanding of any living system may never seem to end, the system itself will one day cease. This physical world has a point of consummation. Why then do we long for this understanding of that which is lasting in nature, perhaps endless? The reason is that we were designed for another world. That world is spiritual and, by its nature, eternal.

"[F]or the things which are seen are temporal; but the things which are not seen are eternal" (2 Corinthians 4:18, KJV).

By no coincidence, Jesus is described as "the One Who is, Who was, and is to come."

It is a bit of a brainteaser to consider God. I mean, where did He come from? When did He arrive, and how did He get to be God?

It is the same problem with Jesus the Messiah.

The prophet Micah said concerning the coming Messiah that His goings forth are from everlasting.

In other words, He would come from the unseen, someday show up in the here and now, and just keep going.

He would come from the world beyond into the world we know, and then return from where He came. All along the way He would invite passengers to join Him.

Al Isaksen was one passenger who got on board.

As a pastor, Al loved to preach about the Hebrew names for God. One that comes to mind is *El Shammah*, which means the "God Who is there."

It connects very closely to another Hebrew name, *Emanuel*, or "God with us."

The idea is that wherever we are, or have been, or have yet to be, God is there. God is not only "there," He is also "here."

This concept has inspired philosophers and New Age mystics for ages, but it is biblically rooted. However, it remains a mere possibility until it becomes anchored in truth.

For Pastor Al, it became firmly rooted within his soul. He lived "as if" God was with him daily and always. He lived that way to the very end. However, that way of living did not begin until his new life began.

The day was August 16, 1964. It was 8:00 A.M.

He describes the morning as normal until he went into the shower. Then, as he describes what happened, "The *Shekinah* glory of God filled the room." He experienced the presence of God in a way that he never thought possible, and it brought him to tears of repentance. Not only did he become born again, but he was baptized with the Holy Spirit. For some theologians out there, these are the same event, but many others see this work of the Holy Spirit as a subsequent happening. Pastor Al would agree. His new birth was not unlike many in the book of Acts, but it is not the normal course of most in our day. Most people who experience the new birth do not immediately receive the baptism in the Holy Spirit. It comes later, if indeed it is experienced. I am mentioning this, not to cause controversy, but as a biographer. This was the sequence of Al Isaksen's spiritual history. He never felt that this made him in any way better or more important. It was simply God's sovereign way of weaving Himself into the affairs of man, in this case, Pastor Al's.

In the days following his conversion, changes began to take place. His appetite was first. He began to desire things that had no previous interest to him, and those things that had held his interest began fading away.

In his words, "I used to drink at Joe's Place, now I drink at Joel's Place."

He was referring to the local bar and the biblical prophet Joel. No longer was he interested in drinking from this world's wells, which he called polluted, but his thirst was for "living waters," from which the fountain never went dry. The Bible, which previously was an unopened book on the shelf, began to mysteriously draw him.

As he began to read it regularly, something unfolded that was even more out of character for him: he started to study.

As his desire to study grew stronger, he sensed the need to change his schedule. Because he was a milkman, he had a strict commitment to deliver his dairy at appointed times, but an idea came to him. If he could combine some of his Friday clients with his Thursday ones, he could free up one day for study. It was a long shot, but worth the pursuit. And it worked. One by one his Friday customers agreed to have their milk delivered on Thursday.

In a short time he was working four long days, but he had freed his schedule to study for three consecutive days each week.

This went on for three years. He told Dorothy that unless there was a dire emergency, his time in the basement was reserved for God. As I write, I can imagine reading this and thinking how slighted she may have felt. But it was not that way at all.

At this point Dorothy had yet to come to faith in Jesus, but she insisted that her husband learn all that he could and as fast as he could because she too was eager to understand what this faith was all about. She saw a real change taking place in him; it attracted her, even though she did not understand. She supported his pursuit of God, but was puzzled by his zeal. The problem was compounded because the church they attended taught very little from the Bible, and their services had no likeness to the newborn excitement that began to consume him.

So the Milkman began to study. He would also visit used bookstores, where he was able to find books from preachers and teachers throughout history. He read their biographies and studied their lessons. He listened to the radio each Sunday night to hear Bible teachers preach from New York City, and he began to visit their churches as often as he could. He heard of a Bible school on the North Shore of Long Island and began visiting there.

He made new contacts and new friends, people who loved Jesus and were committed to serving Him. Al could not get enough.

His waking hours were consumed not only with study, but also with worship. Tears of cleansing and gratitude began to flow out of his heart.

"He hath put a new song in my mouth, even praise unto my God" (Psalm 40:3, ASV).

One morning on his milk route, an unusual scene unfolded. As he was walking up the sidewalk to one of his customer's homes, he was singing a song of praise. That was not abnormal for him, but to hear another voice at that hour was. It was his customer.

She peeked her head out the door and called him.

"Al, would you bring the milk in and put it on the counter?"

Until then he had never seen his customer. He simply put the milk in her box with the bill and picked up her check with each new delivery.

As he brought the milk in, she immediately questioned him.

"Al, what religion are you?"

He said that he didn't belong to any religion because he no longer believed in religion.

"No," she pressed, "something within me told me that you could help me. Do you think you can?"

"Do you have the time?" he asked.

She said she did, so he returned to his truck and shut it off.

When he came back, he began to tell her the story of salvation in Jesus, the hope of His calling, and the power of His resurrection. As she listened carefully to what he said, he realized that he was there delivering more than dairy. For the first time, he understood what the Scripture taught about the "milk of the word." She was receiving it as a newborn baby.

He was then privileged to both lead her to Jesus and pray for her.

Through a broken voice and tears, he recalls this story as confirmation to his calling as a different kind of milkman.

Not only did his study continue in his home, but once Dorothy got saved, they began having other people in their home for group study of the Word of God.

It began with seven people, and within a year it grew to a hundred.

Their basement was packed, and the crowd overflowed into their living room and bedroom of their tiny ranch house.

One night before the meeting, God spoke to Al about four men who were going to call and ask him to be their minister in Sayville. One of them was a pastor, who had recently gotten saved after being in the ministry for seventeen years. The four of them would drive from Suffolk County to the Isaksen home each Friday night, because they were so drawn to what God was doing in Massapequa. It was not long before the phone rang and one of the men asked if they could come and talk with him.

Without telling them he knew their reason, he invited them to talk after the meeting. Sure enough they told him they would like him to consider being their minister in West Sayville. He in turn replied that God had already prepared him. He told them to pray together for one month, and if they were sure that this was still their desire, he would come.

After the month passed, they affirmed their decision, and Al the milkman became Pastor Al.

Before long, the Isaksens sold their house in Massapequa. Together with four other families, they bought the vacated property and parsonage of a Dutch Reformed Church. For Pastor Al it was complete investment. It became a mark of his devotion; what he believed in, he invested in.

However, it wasn't long before opposition showed up. Two of the men who originally asked him to come and be their pastor had views contrary to the vision Pastor Al was given from the Lord. They felt it necessary to maintain a perspective of ministry that they had brought with them from their prior church experience. Pastor Al did not see it in alignment with God's word, and he was troubled by their persistence. If a man-made format was going to dictate this ministry, he wanted no part of it. His relationship with Jesus was too precious to trade for another religious expression. At 2:00 A.M., after much talk, he told them he was going to the parsonage to sleep. If they wanted, he would have his bags packed and leave in the morning. He went to the house, and an hour later one of the men came to him and insisted that he stay. There would be no further discussion.

So he slept that night.

And for the next twenty-five years that marked his ministry, he would rest fully in the promise that God was the initiator of this work and that it all belonged to Him. If He were to bring it to a halt, then Pastor Al would be the first to lock the doors. That never happened, and until the day he left, the doors remained unlocked day and night for:

"The Spirit and the Bride say, 'Come.' And let the one who hears say, 'Come.' And let the one who is thirsty come." (Revelation 22:17, ESV)

For if it ever became clear that Jesus was not in the midst of the ministry of Gospel Community Church, there was no longer a reason for it to exist.

CHAPTER 8

A Mass or a Mess?

M ilk is not like a martini.

You won't see many movies where the husband or the wife comes home after a busy day at the office and heads for the kitchen, lifts a cocktail glass from the shelf, and pours a cold glass of milk. Nor will you see a couple dressed in tuxedo and evening gown taking from the waiter's tray or the bartender's hand a frosted glass of fresh milk.

It just does not happen that way.

For one, milk will not produce the same effect. For another, milk is just too messy.

Gospel Community Church was a very quaint structure. From the outside it looked like a Norman Rockwell painting. Behind the welcome sign on the tidy patch of grass that stood by the sidewalk, was a white bevel-sided wooden structure built around the turn of the twentieth century by Dutch craftsmen. Above the wooden entry doors was a large, circular stained-glass window. High above that stood a steeple with a huge bronze bell attached to an old rope, like the ones that tied the boats to the dock at the end of the road. On Sunday mornings, whoever was around would give it a strong tug and call the neighbors to worship.

Or at least call them to consider it.

The sanctuary was lined with wooden pews. Behind the altar were the remaining pipes of the organ that once sat where a piano now stood. The windows on each side of the room stood tall, facing each other with their curved crowns as if they were soldiers at arms.

Everything looked neat and proper. All the details were planned and in place.

Architecturally, that is.

For at any given moment one might expect the choir to stroll gracefully onto the altar with song sheets in colored folders against each chest, their robes swaying gently as they assume their assigned place. The choir director would stand in front of them and with a great, big Colgate smile, he would ask the congregation to please rise as we sing the salutatory hymn. Gradually all would begin to stand, as suited fathers coax their little boys up while their lovely wives un-ruffle the coordinating Sunday dresses of their daughters. Many can be heard clearing their throats with the expectation of matching the perfect tonal quality of the choir in the front. All would display that same solemn smile as they await the director's signal.

But that moment never seemed to come to Gospel Community.

I remember Pastor Al telling the story of a woman from the neighborhood stopping by his house and asking him what times the church held Mass on Sunday.

"Ma'am," he answered politely, "if you are looking for a Mass, you will have to go down the street a bit. But if you are looking for a mess, you have come to the right place." I did not get it then, but I do now.

Around the corner, about a mile east on Main Street, stood a large Catholic Church. It must have had a huge membership, because each Sunday morning a policeman would stand on the street directing traffic. They not only conducted Mass there, but they had one every hour on Sunday morning and one or two on Saturday night. In a sense it was like a "Mass" factory. It had to run like a train schedule. Whatever the purpose they had in mind for their service, it was critical to be accomplished within that hour in order to avoid a traffic jam in their parking lot, worse than rush hour on the Long Island Expressway. That called for careful planning of their service. Rehearsal was crucial. Songs and sermons had to be timed. No room could be allowed for improvisation or interruption or mistakes. I wondered what would happen if God decided to appear in one of their services.

What a mess!

Which brings me to my point.

Milk is a messy drink. It leaves a moustache.

It is not a social drink.

At Gospel Community Church, milk was served. Not that it was the only drink or the only nutrition. Living water was on tap, and bread and wine were on the table. Meat was the main course. But these are spiritual terms and require further explanation. However, no one who spent any length of time at the fellowship could escape the taste of fresh milk nor depart without its mark on their lips.

That is not to say that people looked like vagabonds and dressed like slobs. If you did, though, you would still be welcomed, because that is how Jesus would treat people. And that is what Pastor Al knew and believed. Jesus treated people with respect and acceptance. It was neither with hypocrisy nor favoritism. Jesus loved people the way they were, but He loved them too much to leave them as He found them. The Milkman took his cue from the God he learned from in his basement study. If he were to love people and deliver to them the pure "milk of the word," then the Holy Spirit of God was in a position to change them into the image of Jesus. That was neither Pastor Al's responsibility nor his job description.

That is where the "mess" shows up.

If we take the teachings of Jesus coupled with the teachings of the "early fathers," then wrap them up to fit into a neatly packaged social setting, we get a "Mass," whether it is Catholic or Protestant. However, when the belief is settled that the Holy Spirit is God through personal revelation, we begin to live by a totally different schedule. Does that mean that we are no longer to regard time, no longer bound to keep its restraints? Not on this earth.

We are still living in a time/space continuum and will be until we leave. Into man's hand has been given much authority. However, controlling time is not one of his powers. All we are told is to redeem the time, and that means submitting to God, not only on the hour, but also with each moment.

That is how Pastor Al believed. The Bible teaches us that God is not a god of chaos. If I believe that the Holy Spirit is God and that my time is in His hand, then the length of time for a Sunday morning service should be His to determine. Too often we Americans are more focused on what comes next than what is now. Ironically, our church service becomes more like a "Mass" and our spiritual life a mess.

Pastor Al used to say that Jesus did not come to turn the world upside down—it already is. He came to turn it right-side up.

That can be pretty messy.

It can also be very much alive.

CHAPTER 9

Care vs. Control

"Doesn't anybody care?"

For many people if not most, at least at one time or another, the subject of care is of utmost importance. Before we get personal, let's begin with the general concept of care.

First of all, no one could have invented the need for care or the desire to be cared for. It is universal. Nobody has ever entered this world and stuck around for long without the care of another. That is true across the board, be it people or animals.

Currently we have a blue jay nest on our back porch. The eggs have cracked open and introduced to us five tiny, wet baby birds that barely know how to chirp. All they do is stretch out their necks. I discovered that when the momma left. I went in to take their picture, but they were so cuddled together they became indistinguishable. To get them to pose, I simply made a birdlike noise. Immediately they picked up their heads in unison and stretched out their necks, so far that I was afraid they would snap like rubber bands.

What a great illustration of our need for care. We will stretch out to the skies to find it. Male or female, it makes no difference. We share equally our need and our openness to express it. That is when we are young.

When we grow up, or at least think we have, a distinction begins to emerge. Since I am not an experienced bird-watcher, I will limit my discussion to people.

At some early point in our human development, pride lifts its head up with an outstretched neck. The pride of man begins to emerge in the realm of care. It is not that females do not share in this destructive potential of the human soul, but males seem to have mastered its latent power over the centuries. Lately, however, women have been closing the gap very rapidly.

The first assault of this rising pride is about the source of care.

"I can take care of that myself" is its elementary statement.

"I don't need anyone to take care of me" is its graduation speech.

What is interesting is that the need for care is not denied by this pride of man. It is the source from whence it comes that is at issue. In actuality we all need care, so why do we get bent out of shape by the source? Could it be that the lines drawn between care and control are too often blurred?

Control.

Have you ever noticed the bumper sticker that says "God is my copilot"?

I remember the first time that I spotted one. It was in a church parking lot. I had pulled in late one Sunday morning and found the last spot in the lot. As I was walking in, a car pulled up in search of a parking place. I watched as the woman tried to squeeze her car into a space that would defy the laws of physics. Sure enough, she bumped the car that was quietly parked there. I stood there watching unnoticed. I did not recognize her, so I was a bit curious to see her next move. She was determined. She tried again.

Someone had recently said that the definition of lunacy is attempting the same mistake a second time and expecting different results. Concerned that I was witnessing a live presentation of that definition, I approached her car. On my way over, I noticed that bumper sticker. Something inside of me clicked.

"God is my copilot."

Now I was a fairly new believer, having come to church for less than a year, and I felt somewhat green in my understanding. This woman was a bit older and I suspected more experienced with God and the Bible. Her bumper sticker looked well worn. Not only did my car not have one, I was not even sure where to purchase one.

I read the bumper sticker again as I took a few steps closer to her car.

What she was about to do a second time reminded me of my first full-time job.

I was fifteen years old working at Adventurer's Inn as a busboy. I had to hitchhike to work and made thirty-eight dollars for a forty-hour week. It was not quite as hard as my father's generation had it though. They had to walk to school in five feet of snow and uphill in both directions, so the story goes. My commute, however, was not a hardship.

Even though my job was totally non-glamorous, it did have one good perk.

Bumper cars.

On my half-hour lunch break, I was able to scarf down a company hot dog and then finish my time riding the bumper cars for free. The electric cars with rubber bumpers gave a liberating relief to the routine of the day.

I was beginning to think that maybe this woman never had that childhood experience behind her. As I was getting closer to her car, she turned and saw me. That is when the revelation came.

Her bumper sticker was not written under divine inspiration.

"Excuse me, ma'am," I said somewhat sheepishly, as she was about to bump that unsuspecting car a second time.

A holy boldness came upon me.

"I think I know what your problem is."

"What problem is that?" she asked, rather naively.

"Your bumper sticker," I said. "I think you need to make God the Pilot, and you be the copilot."

Control.

Who does not have a problem with control?

We all want to have it, even though deep down inside we know that we cannot handle it as we ought.

Remote control.

Have you ever entered the TV room and tried to get the remote out of someone else's hand?

"Pretty please" just does not seem to work.

Why is it so difficult to let someone else have control of what appears to be in my hand?

I have heard people argue against God. I should probably qualify that by saying "the Christian" God. The concept that is presented is that Christians are like robots, and God is a control freak. Christians all think alike because God is clicking the remote at His will. Just look at their voting record.

Maybe it would help to look at the Pilot/copilot illustration.

I would argue that it is not an accurate one. When Jesus came to earth, He came into a culture and time that had no airplanes. He could have chosen another time. If He came in our day, He could have been a pilot, a bus driver, a train engineer, or perhaps a cabbie. In His day, I suppose He could have started a business as a ferryboat captain on the Sea of Galilee. He chose instead to be a carpenter.

He was a builder, a repairer, a maker of useful and beautiful things.

Does that say anything to us?

Jesus also said that He was a Shepherd. In Jeremiah, God calls Himself a Potter.

The picture that I see is one of leading, providing, and shaping, not one of mindless control over those who followed Him. In fact, Jesus said to His disciples that there would come a day when He would leave them; that is, He would return to heaven. However, He qualified His departure by telling them that another One would come, the Holy Spirit, Who would abide with them. He would be their Comforter and their Teacher and their Friend. By definition, His name would be "the One Who comes alongside." If you were sitting with a close friend watching TV, the chances are that you would not have to argue over who held the remote because you would likely share the same interests. That does not mean that you might not want to watch something different, but because of your friendship, you would not cause hostility.

That is where our illustration breaks down. The Person Whom Jesus said was to come was the Holy Spirit, or the Spirit of Jesus. He would not simply sit next to you on the couch "chillin' out" in front of a playoff game; He would make His home inside of you. That could sound a bit creepy if He were not so perfect. In fact, His role in Jesus' absence is to perfect us. When I say "us," I am speaking of those who have been born again, those who have been so captured by Jesus' love and awakened to His deity that they have said yes to His lordship.

We have now come full cycle with the concept of control. To be a follower of God is to follow Jesus and allow Him control. It is an inside job that requires decisive action.

Jesus said, "If anyone wants to be My disciple, he must deny himself, pick up his cross, and follow Me."

The process of denial is the release of control. The disciple is one who acknowledges that the One Who made him is more capable of taking the helm than he himself. After screwing up enough opportunities in life to control my own circumstances and respond properly to the many knuckleballs thrown my way, I have experienced my vast limitations. At times I have wondered if I could even pilot my way into a church parking lot on a Sunday morning.

Release of control can be a dangerous thing. The Bible is in full agreement. In fact we are told to be self-controlled. Is that a contradiction?

This is where our pilot illustration needs clarity.

If God is my copilot, then He is subject to me. On the other hand, if our seats are reversed, then so are our roles. I am still a vital player in the safety and destination of the vehicle, but I rely on the expertise and experience of my superior. His control will lead to my success. Proper self-control limits me to my capabilities.

When the Messiah comes into my being, I am given the revelation that He is more capable of driving this vehicle since He also designed and manufactured it. When it comes to destination, He alone is able to securely drive me to my rightful and blissful finish line, regardless of passing storms.

The reason that I am able to release control is because, at the point of faith, He actually releases within my spirit the will to do so. It is still my choice, but I am convinced by perfect Intelligence that my choice for Jesus is my best option.

It is a defining moment.

Let me put it this way. Have you ever fallen asleep at the wheel? Nothing can be scarier, especially the way it once happened to me. I was driving a large rental truck packed with our family possessions and our car in tow across the mountains of Pennsylvania. It was four o'clock in the morning, and the snow was falling. I was exhausted but determined to keep going. Then it happened.

I fell asleep at the wheel.

A strange thing happens in that situation. You do not know that you have fallen asleep until you awake. That is when the fear struck. I awoke suddenly. Not only did I realize that I was asleep with all our goods in tow, but my heart froze to see my six-year-old daughter sleeping peacefully in the seat beside me. When I looked through the windshield into the black of night, I almost passed out in shock to see that we were heading off the road down a curvy Pennsylvania mountain. My heart still trembles at the memory.

I am so thankful that I was not the pilot that night. In fact, I should have lost my position as copilot, but that is a different issue.

Here is what I have come to understand: I am neither the captain of my ship, nor the master of my fate. To think and behave that way is not only suicidal, it can be fatal to all on board. We are not capable of taking this vessel to shore. What we are capable of is being decisive. Giving God control is the right decision. Ignoring the need to release control is also a decision, but it is the wrong one. At the end of this life, we will all concur with God that full control indeed belonged to Him.

There is something else that I have learned: when we do give Jesus control, we receive His care.

Does that mean that God only cares for Christians? Are they the only ones who are well fed and healthy? The answer is an obvious "no," for God cares for all His creation. "His eye is on the sparrow" and "the rain falls on the just and the unjust alike."

When a person chooses to release control in the spiritual realm, he in turn is given the promise that his spirit is entrusted to God. When Jesus becomes your Messiah or Savior, God becomes your spiritual Father. At that moment you can have rest for your soul.

No longer do I have to wrestle with my eyes to stay awake through the wintry storms and dark of night. My fate is in the hands of One Who is able, Who is strong and Who loves me. I am then free to be me and let God be God.

What does all this have to do with the Milkman?

As we have discussed, the milkman is a metaphor. Just as he has received the milk from the dairy, he is hired to deliver it to his customer. That is his assignment. He does not need to blow his horn when he arrives and expect the family to rise as he steps off his truck, nor are they contracted to greet him at the door when he finishes his delivery.

He makes no announcements, receives no offerings, and expects no applause. In fact, his job is to deliver his product as he received it, as unobtrusively as possible. Basically, his job is to be invisible and let the milk do the job.

Is that an illustration of your pastor or the church leadership you have known?

Sad to say, but I expect the answer is negative.

Many of you who have had poor experience with your pastoral leadership have also discarded any relation with a church body. Added to that, you have dismissed the Bible as being untruthful. You say you love Jesus, but ascribe everything associated with Him as being man's invention.

Why is that?

The reason often given is that the ones who preach its message are behaving contrary to how the message reads. When asked to explain, most would say the pastors are control freaks.

Is this universal? Was the Church always like this?

Fortunately the answer is a resounding "NO!"

Unfortunately the answer is also a deafening response of "quite often, yes."

Pastor Al was an exception.

I did not realize that at first because he was the only pastor that I knew. It would take several years before I would discover how privileged I was to have a pastor with such a unique perspective. Yet I found that to be a very sad and unsettling discovery.

How could that have happened? How could so many church leaders insist on maintaining such tight control?

The obvious reason is that the pride of man has not experienced a final blow. The not-so-obvious reason is that for many pastors across the land, they have never fully tasted and digested the product that they have been called to deliver. As a result, they have not received its nutritional benefit and innate power to resist this awful pride.

In other words, God is still the copilot.

One Sunday morning, I found myself leading the service at Gospel Community Church.

It was not a position that I requested, but one in which I was enlisted.

Pastor Al believed that one of the biblical elements of the healthy growth of a congregation was to establish men to be sound in their understanding of the faith and willing and able to lead their families and their surrounding community into a relationship with Jesus.

Making men biblical leaders was his passion.

He rarely discussed that, but he made every opportunity to accomplish it. Sometimes I think he sped up the process.

The role of leading a service was somewhat vague. As a result, it could be rather uncomfortable, humanly speaking. One did not receive formal training or a job description. There were no rules, no "dos and don'ts." What he did expect, and he knew this would come through exercise, was to allow the Holy Spirit to lead you.

For me to release control to the Holy Spirit was a rather new experience. For Pastor Al it was a done deal. That Sunday morning I discovered why.

The service was flowing along as it usually did. I opened it up with a somewhat relaxed reading of a verse or two from the Bible and an informal greeting to the congregants. The people out there seemed to be relaxed, so I settled down and my knees buckled a little less. As we began to worship, I felt so much better. My eyes closed and my concentration became centered.

In fact, worship did its perfect work in me as God intended. For my eyes were on Jesus, no longer my performance, and I was at peace. I knew He was there and that He cared for me. I did not need to assume control.

During those services, time was not regulated. We began at a certain point, but the clock stopped ticking after that. Worship was a congregational experience. Yes, there were skilled musicians, but they did not control the course of events. They came to worship as well. As David Wilkerson once said at a Times Square service, "When God shows up, no flesh shall boast at His appearance."

In that New York City fellowship, located in the middle of Broadway, were many highly gifted and trained musicians, yet it was clear that the altar was not a stage but a place of sacrifice. There was no power released in performance. The worship of God is not a divine ego trip, but an opportunity for the people of God to enter into an experience that is otherworldly, one that reaches from within the human spirit and connects to His Holy Spirit. When one is so engaged, something transforming is able to take place. God begins to access the areas of our soul that were closed off and seemingly impenetrable.

At times like that in a Gospel Community service, it was not uncommon to witness a variety of responses to that secret work of God. One might stand erect with her hands lifted high in adoration, while another is bowed low with his face in his hands. Someone may boldly proclaim a prophetic word, while another quietly reads a portion from the Bible.

It was not uncommon for a period of silence to be broken by a chorus or a song or a hymn started by different individuals in the fellowship. The times I recall most favorably were unscripted, and yet they appeared to be fully orchestrated.

When praise rang out in its highest form, it sounded angelic. I am not the only one who was convinced that at times angels were in our midst.

My understanding of God within man grew tremendously in that fellowship under Pastor Al's guidance. That day in particular, it took a big leap.

Before I ever began to actually take part in the leading of the service, I would have believed that the order of the service was rehearsed. I thought those who led in singing knew every song they would sing and the message Pastor Al would be preaching. They did not. Somehow I felt those who spoke out or sang out were a part of this pre-planned event, because it all seemed so connected. Yet it always had this uncanny result in reaching me deeply in a way that no other gathering did.

I was slowly becoming suspicious that this was even bigger than I thought. Maybe God actually was orchestrating these gatherings.

I became convinced on that Sunday morning.

There was a period of silence that morning after what was called the worship portion of the service. I sensed it was time for me to arise and assume some measure of leadership. I was still humbled by my position in front of all these people. It was nothing I was accustomed to or yet comfortable with, even more so when a man whom I did not know raised his hand and asked if he could ask a question. I knew he was free to do so, but unless it had to do with the bathroom location, I also knew that there was little chance that I could answer his question. I told him yes, and then my knees began to buckle again.

"Is it okay to pray to the Holy Spirit?" he asked.

I still do not know if he was serious or if he was attempting to be divisive. What I do know is that I stood in silent disbelief. There I was, standing there dumbfounded when I was supposed to be "leading" the service. I don't know if I looked as helpless as I felt or how long I simply stood there speechless. I had never heard anyone ask that question before, nor have I heard anyone ask it since. I was still a young believer, and in those seconds the only question that I had was, "What am I doing here?"

It became a defining moment for me, a most teachable lesson, given my vulnerability and the subject.

The Trinity.

No doubt the Trinity, or what I have come to prefer to call the triune nature of God, is probably the most incomprehensible, mysterious aspect of the faith. How can one explain what he cannot comprehend?

In Jewish tradition the most important declaration of faith is the *Shema*:

"Hear, O Israel: the Lord our God, the Lord is One."

That is solid biblical teaching, straight from the book of Deuteronomy.

It has also been misunderstood and, hence, wrongly applied.

Whenever the Israelites strayed from this foundational doctrine of their revealed faith, they strayed into not only the *cultures* of their surrounding neighbors, but also the customs of these same neighbors. This included the worship of idols, which represented a variety of gods, no different from their Egyptian taskmasters.

Through the centuries, God would raise up a variety of prophets who would call the people to repent of this idolatry and return to the One true and living God. At times there was a national cry of remorse and a return to the God of Israel, but those times were rare.

Finally, God gave them the sentence that He had long ago pronounced in the same book of Deuteronomy. They would be banished from their land.

The Babylonian Captivity in 586 B.C. had a huge impact on the Jewish population and provided many lessons for all who care to listen. The major one, though, is that God takes his word seriously.

For seventy years (also according to prophesy), the Jews were taken into captivity to a foreign land with a people of a foreign language and strange customs. It was not long before the reality struck that their identity as a people was at risk. If they were to survive, they needed to preserve not only their distinct language and customs, but also their sole identity as a people who were known as being monotheistic—in fact, the only people who held such a belief.

Have I lost you yet? Bear with me. I am heading back to the question posed at that morning service, but I feel it necessary to provide some context.

As a Jew, therefore, the greatest distinction one had was his or her belief that there was only one God. You did not even have to believe "in" Him yet, but believe that there could be no more than one "of" Him. When this foundational belief was absent, then one could no longer be a Jew, but an apostate, driven from the God of Israel into the idolatry of the nations.

The danger that the rabbis discussed during their exile and the years following their return is that apostasy was contagious. If it rebooted into Jewish life after they returned to their land, they would again be destined to banishment among a cruel and foreign people. Therefore, at all costs, the unseen God of the universe alone would be the God of the Jews.

That is why the Pharisaic rabbis watched Jesus so closely. It seemed that wherever Jesus showed up, a group of Pharisees were nearby. For a time, they gave Him some leeway to speak publicly, until one day He made this declaration:

"...I and My Father are One."

Not only was this declaration a dilemma for the rabbis of Jesus' day, but one that confronts any prospective Jewish seeker ever since, including me. To make matters even worse, He taught His disciples that when He left this earth He would pray to His Father that Another would be sent, the Holy Spirit. He in turn would lead them into all truth and remind them of the things that Jesus had already taught.

To follow Jesus was to intentionally believe that He was God and yet that the Father was also God. They had not even stopped to fully consider what Jesus was talking about when He introduced this personal relationship with the Holy Spirit, or in Hebrew, *Ruach Hakodesh.*

They had no time to think. On that night, the first night of Passover, Jesus was arrested, tried, and sentenced to execution. It was a night like no other in the history of the Jews.

As eerie as the setting of the first Passover meal had been under that black Egyptian sky, this was even worse. For this night was again different from all other nights. On this night, the angel of death not only avoided passing over the household of Joseph, he took the firstborn of Mary's womb. What unimaginable and unexpected cruelty the disciples witnessed as Jesus, not only their Teacher, but their Brother and closest Friend, was beaten and mocked throughout the remainder of that darkest of nights. When dawn awoke, He faced no mercy, only the horror and finality of the Roman cross.

While He hung on the tree that He once fashioned, now modified to be a tree upon which He would die, His accusers stood by mocking Him to the very end.

They had to dismiss any semblance of God. They were already successful in marring any image of humanity, as His face and back were swollen and bleeding to the point of being beyond recognition.

"If You are God, take Yourself down from there," they jeered.

This was their final attempt to justify themselves. He had been accused of blasphemy, making Himself equal with God, the highest form of Jewish treason. If He could be executed and the world kept turning, then they would have their final proof and closing statement: Jesus, a mere man, was not God.

None of this was supposed to take His companions by surprise, nor His mother. They were told, in fact repeatedly told, by their Rabbi that he would be arrested, smitten, and killed by the hands of those who hated Him. But disbelief is common among the children of man, and its painful embrace broke the will of those who had pledged allegiance only hours before. If it had not, they might have recalled that He also taught them that, though He would die and be buried, He would rise again. It was a painful lesson to forget their Master's words.

That is precisely the reason the Holy Spirit would be sent to them. Not only would He remind them of what Jesus taught, He would empower them to respond in belief.

However, following the death of Jesus, the disciples fled in fear, wondering if they would be the next victims to experience the brutal ending that their Rabbi endured. For the forces of evil had marshaled themselves together, and not only from the religious/political leadership of the Jews. All of Rome was aroused to squash any insurgency that would jeopardize their complete control over Israel.

Who could blame the disciples for fleeing? Would I have responded differently? It was the natural reaction to human tragedy: disbelief, sorrow, fear, and despair. I can only imagine what they may have been thinking: "If Love is so fragile and Hope so fleeting, then what am I here for? Will I also be left alone to face its mocking blow?"

I cannot say for certain that this entire scenario crossed my mind as I waited endlessly for the right response to this man's question. What I do know is that embracing Jesus as the Jewish Messiah was not as difficult as embracing Him as God. That is the historically rooted stumbling block for all Jews, and, I might add, Muslims. For a monotheist to embrace the possibility of this triune nature of God would be like a baby bird trying to fly from its nest. Perhaps it is possible, but no less frightening.

For me to declare that Jesus was God and not just a great man or avatar was a huge step. I knew that it was contrary to what I was taught in all my years of Hebrew school. In each synagogue service we would sing the *Shema* and often repeat it in English:

"*Hear, O Israel: the Lord our God, the Lord is One.*"

It was written, not only in the Torah but also on every *mezuzah* that is nailed to the doorpost of every Jewish home.

Don't let these words depart from your lips.

I literally became tongue-tied when I attempted to declare that Jesus was God and Messiah.

But boy, what a relief when I did! Immediately I experienced liberation.

At that point, however, I had not given the Holy Spirit as much attention. But when I did, I received a new sense of liberty and power beginning to work within me.

Even though I knew that the Holy Spirit was filling me and His presence was deeply affecting me, I had not fully begun to consider that He was Deity—that is until that morning.

As I stood there looking at that man, wondering about his question and recognizing my frozen state, I felt a hand rest upon my shoulder. Pastor Al did what I had never seen him do before or since. He stood up and leaned over my shoulder to address that man's question.

"Excuse me, Brother," he said to the man with a voice of assurance and compassion, "but the Holy Spirit is God."

He then sat back down. A great peace settled and the presence of the Lord filled the room. Out of the hush, people began again to worship.

He did not usurp my leadership. In fact, he not only taught me that day about the Holy Spirit, but Pastor Al left me with a picture of His role within my life and the life of the Church.

Pastor Al could have gotten up from his seat like a baseball manager leaves the dugout. His pitcher is showing signs of losing control, and it is time for him to give up the ball and sit in the dugout. Someone more qualified needs to step up and take his place. That is, I am afraid, how some pastors see themselves.

That is not how the Milkman did it. Instead, he came alongside me, gently assumed control and released me of my burden. When he spoke, it was instructive and not demonstrative. There was clarity that needed to be reached and some truth to be told, and that is exactly what he did in a manner that ended the discussion. In plain words, Pastor Al released his control of the service, and in turn freedom resulted and worship of God broke out.

Jesus cares for His Church. He died to prove it. In fact, if He had not died, there would be no Church. When God's Spirit is given freedom to control—and by the Spirit I mean the unheralded Member of this monotheistic Deity in the form of three Persons—divine care is released into the deepest recesses of the heart, the place where no one else can travel.

I learned that day through revelation that the Holy Spirit is indeed God. He is not separate from creation, redemption, or the continuity and consummation of all created things. He was there from before the beginning. He hovered over all creation and strived with man throughout history. This is biblical teaching, straight from the Torah and made alive and reachable through Jesus. He is not to be feared, but embraced and endeared. He makes no claims for Himself; He only points to Jesus so that all people can see the face of God and the depths of His love. This is the good news. The gospel of Jesus centers on His sinless life, sacrificial death, and resurrection. It does not stop there. If one embraces this redemptive invitation, the Holy Spirit becomes not only his source of transforming power; He becomes a personal Rabbi, as if Jesus came to live within. And that is exactly what He does.

Yet too many pastors are unfamiliar with the Holy Spirit. They are either unacquainted with Him, make Him into a sideshow, or are simply unwilling to release control to Him.

Each one of these conclusions leaves a wake of tragic consequence.

The Holy Spirit came to make the weak in spirit strong, the poor in spirit rich. He takes the impossible demands of the law of God and writes them upon the heart of man so that they become a person's desire, not just his or her requirement. Pastor Al delivered that message whenever you saw him, not simply on Sunday morning. He believed that God's Spirit speaks to all His children and wants also to speak through them.

If one were to drop in on Pastor Al for a casual visit, it would not be unusual for him to ask, "What has the Lord been speaking to you lately?"

He asked because he believed that God spoke to His Church—or what the New Testament calls His "body"—through each individual member. He considered it his pastoral duty to make room for that voice to be heard. As a member of that same body, he simply wanted to hear the voice of God whenever He could.

Pastor Al never considered himself superior or more important than anyone. He knew that for the church to grow and be effective, Jesus had to be the head of the body. When that spiritual anatomy is working together in sync, he noted that the church is transformed from an organization to an *organism*. For that to occur was simply a matter of allowing it to happen. In other words, the form and function of the church is released into the hand of God. It is the full cycle of control and care. When the pastor or worship leader releases control to the Spirit of God, he and the church are under the Lord's responsible care.

In order to receive the proper care, the most capable must be in control; in order to get to the destination, the best pilot should be in the driver's seat.

I was not standing before the congregation on that day because of my great experience or expert knowledge. I was there because Pastor Al trusted that the Holy Spirit wanted to work in me and, in spite of my ignorance, through me.

I am grateful for that morning. Before I ever stood before the congregation, I confessed to God that I felt incapable and inexperienced. I gave Him control of what would be. What I did not yet realize was how much He wanted that opportunity, because He wanted to care for me.

The Holy Spirit has continued to teach me ever since. I did not need to know how to navigate through every obstacle. I did not have to behave or talk as if I could. I needed to trust Him then, and I need to trust Him now. When I do, I realize not only *how well* He can bring a matter under control, but *why* He does.

It is because He cares.

God cares—not just about us, but also for us.

"Cast all your cares upon Him, because He cares for you," the apostle Peter wrote to the Church.

If only pastors across our land would take that step of releasing the control of their churches to the Spirit and allowing the members of His body to exercise their faith. It is time to put to rest the "one-man show" mentality of modern American Christianity. Not only is it powerless and fruitless, but also it has become reckless and dangerous. What has been considered normal and acceptable for a few decades is now rejected by a new generation. They view Sunday morning as a time for old folks to deal with their guilt about how they behaved during the week, while someone who represents God stands before them and justifies their attendance. Meanwhile, the pastor who stands before them feels it is his sole responsibility to keep them coming. It becomes a customer-relationship thing rather than the delivery of a product.

The latter is what a good milkman does.

He takes fresh milk from the dairy and brings it to the door of the house.

No fanfare, no recognition, no perfect release required, just fresh nutrition in a bottle, waiting for someone to open the door and drink.

"A sheep without a shepherd " (1972)

Paul and El Chevy, not quite road ready

CHAPTER 10

Running on Empty

By the time that I had met Pastor Al, I had already met Jesus.

At that time my wife and I had been living in our semi-suburban home in the central part of Long Island. She was pregnant with our second child, and I was working on the East End as a carpenter's helper. My boss was like a bad dream. To this day, I have yet to meet a man as insidious as he. He was raised as a steel worker in Hungary under a Communist dictatorship. He was an excellent carpenter and extremely strong. As for any other good qualities he possessed, they escaped me. He was filled with bitterness, resentment, and anger. He openly expressed his disdain for Americans. The only people he hated more were the Jews. I did not discover that until a few weeks into the job.

It was 1979, and the economy seemed as if it was on the verge of collapse. New construction had come to a halt, and gas was being rationed. Among the wealthy class in eastern Long Island, you would not have known that. My boss drove us out there in his pickup truck. He was immune to the cars that lined up for gas rationing because the builder he framed for had underground gas tanks that were kept full. We drove without challenge in order to keep the production pumping into his pockets.

Soon I would learn of the builder's anti-Semitism as well.

Until this point of my life I was unaffected by the economy. Money was not a big issue for me. I had become used to "living on a dime." I could survive on granola and kippers, sleep in a sleeping bag on the side of a road or in the woods, and get where I needed to get by sticking out my thumb or working for a few days to save for some gas money.

Of course, when I decided to marry I knew all that would change; I just never suspected how much.

My quest for authenticity had some unexpected turns.

By this time I had come to the conclusion that of all the world religions I had studied—Buddhism, Taoism, Hinduism (Islam had no appeal)—I was unimpressed. There was definitely a mystical sense in each of them, but none of these could adequately explain the nagging questions I had. *Where did we come from? Why are we here? What has gone wrong, and how will it get better?* They had all fallen flat at each point.

My conclusion up to this point was that there had to be a "new age" emerging.

As Bob Dylan wrote, "Something is happening here, but you don't know what it is."

I was still waiting and expecting. One thing was for certain, though. I was not finding it on the job.

For a while I thought that I had come close.

A few years before we married, I decided that I needed to travel alone. After hitchhiking up and down the East Coast and then across the country to California, I headed up the West Coast and through Canada until I could find a place where I was all alone and certain that I was a stranger. Then I waited. My objective was to just be alone without any familiar surroundings and no distractions. I thought that maybe then I could discover who I was and what the "mystery" of this universe was. It was a pretty lofty thought considering the amount of time I allowed.

I ended up making it to Vancouver, where I hiked to a large uninhabited, brackish lake.

I then walked far enough around where I could be seen by no one—as if anyone would actually show up. I felt safe in my seclusion and settled in my tiny backpack-size campsite for a meal of kippers, wheat crackers, and water from my canteen. With a small fire going, I rolled out my sleeping bag and began to wait for revelation. I am not sure what I expected to happen, but I sure know that I did not expect what did happen.

As soon as the sun began its fade upon the western edge of this beautiful tree-lined lake off the Pacific coast, strange creatures began to crawl out of the water and up onto the shore. They seemed to be funny-looking crabs. At first I thought I was about to have a special saltwater treat, until one by one their population increased. What began in my mind as a seafood buffet became a surreal experience. I was barely capable of getting out of my full lotus position when I was encircled by hordes of crabs that looked like aliens from outer space. I felt as if I were in the middle of a Mosaic plague—and I was the Pharaoh!

I had no room to retreat, because behind me was a rock ledge, and I did not want to leave my belongings behind in an attempt to climb. So I grabbed a stick from the fire and began to wave it around like a crazed man as I yelled at them to split. I have a feeling they did not have ears, but that did not concern me. I lost my dharma and all hopes of discovery. Survival was my theme.

They finally departed, but I stayed awake for much of the night on crab watch. The secrets of the universe would remain on hold.

The next morning I was on the road again. A few weeks later I crossed Canada and returned to my rented farmhouse in western New Jersey. My backpack was a bit lighter, but my mind was still laden with the same questions with which I left, if not more.

At this point in time marriage was still not in the picture. Marla and I were very much together, but I was not ready to make the commitment that she really needed. I was too immature, and we did not discuss it. What we did discuss was my next plan.

I had been reading a lot about a new wave of hippies, who had moved out of California and come to the hills of Tennessee and Virginia. They had begun communes—some small, but a few were growing like little towns. My interest grew with each account, and my mind devised a new adventure.

I began to design and build a custom camper that Marla and I could live in. At the same time, I began to restore a 1952 Chevy pickup, which someone was about to send to the scrap yard. With a little help from my friends and several months' time, it was road ready.

Marla and I began a trial journey through New England with her two cats. One cat almost died, and so did our relationship. It was not the life Marla wanted to live, at least not for as long as I had in mind.

We returned to New Jersey where we were able to set her up in an apartment in a renovated chicken coop. It doesn't sound like much, but it really was cozy and there were other units around with friendly young people. It was a secure place for her to stay and continue her job as a nurse. My strongest ambition was for her to be safe and happy. I still did not know about the happiness part, but I felt confident that she would be safe there. As much as I knew that I would miss her, I knew that I had to be on the road again.

This time I was well equipped, and I had a plan. I was going to visit several communes in the mid-South and learn the secret of their success. I was convinced that in this newly emerging counterculture, I would meet a people who had either found true peace and happiness or were on the verge of its discovery.

My journey had a mission this time. I would return with news from afar that would forever change my life and bring it purpose. Because I had renounced the "system" as being the cause of all the world's evils, I would have no part in it. I decided that this included its fast-food restaurants and highways. I was going to drive on roads that were uncorrupted by the capitalist empire, uncontaminated by Styrofoam cups and packaged goods. I renounced the world of plastic for the dawning of the authentic. I was sure that this time I was headed on the right path. If ever I began to doubt myself, my music would restore my vision. Cassette decks had just come out on the market, and I installed the best I could afford. (I forgave myself for the reckless expenditure, as it was for a higher end.) I had copied all my Bob Dylan, Grateful Dead, and Jefferson Airplane albums onto cassettes, and they would accompany me on my journey. Our generation was on the course of uncovering new, liberating truth. It was the heartbeat of the music, and I considered it as much a necessity as gasoline was for the truck.

I felt excitement in my blood, as if I were a part of a new wave of history makers. Like Magellan or Ponce de Leon, I was going to leave behind the Old World and discover the New, bringing back with me its treasures and its secrets.

I never could have imagined how little time it would take to discover such great disappointment.

I traveled from commune to commune. From one stay I would learn of the next. Some were suspicious of me, but most welcomed me usually after they checked out my "crib." It was genuinely countercultural, but I noticed a strange thing was happening. I would go to these communes that were truly "far-out" in every sense of the word, thinking they had arrived, and they would look at my truck and me and think that I had. So I would keep trucking. At each one I would work for my food and try my best to be a part of what they were doing. My lofty vision for the "Age of Aquarius" was beginning to fade. My last hope was Tennessee. That was the Mecca.

CHAPTER 11

"...Looking for a City..."

Sometime in the late sixties, a large group of hippies from the Haight-Ashbury section of San Francisco migrated to the east in search of a homeland. Stephen Gaskin, a former-professor-turned-psychedelic-guru, was their leader. He had an aura of charisma like none other in this generation of seekers. His followers were not only the college-age youth of the sixties. Many of them were married with children; some were trained professionals, others skilled mechanics and craftsmen. They held one thing in common. They were in search of another way of life. In their view, the American capitalist system was a failure. It was now time to begin a new society, one in which Eastern mysticism would meet Western pragmatism. By 1969, they had transplanted their philosophy into a tangible lifestyle. Reminiscent of the expansion of our American borders in the nineteenth century, they packed up everything they deemed a necessity and made an exodus. Instead of their forefathers' handmade covered wagons, this band of pioneers converted about seventy school buses into homes on wheels, many painted in art nouveau, psychedelic graphics, and colors that made them a billboard for this emergent culture wherever they went. In contrast to their ancestors' mantra to "Go west, young man," theirs was to go east. This was not simply a geographical statement, but a philosophical one as well. Their way of life and teaching was to put into practice an ingenuous twist of Zen Buddhism. It involved a communal lifestyle, while allowing most families to have their own space. Personal possessions would become past tense. It was time to elevate human status to a level of being that evolutionists had only dreamed of.

It was a time when God was dead in the Western sense, but alive in the Eastern. He was not a person, but a spirit-presence in everyone and everything. The ancient boundary stones that had set civilization's borders for centuries began to move. I was a part of this movement.

But who could blame us? The life that Jesus purchased for those who would claim to be His followers was hidden from the public eye in America in the late fifties and early sixties. If there was any spiritual life among Christians in those years, it was enclosed within church walls and neatly packaged for Sunday mornings. It was not until the "Jesus Movement" blew in that His life once again became public and apparent. Unfortunately, I tuned out before it checked in.

My attraction to this band of post-Woodstock graduates grew stronger the more that I learned about them. In the winter of 1975, I drove my '52 Chevy pickup truck through the un-gated entrance of the Farm in Summertown, Tennessee—

"Wait a minute, I thought this book was about the Milkman."

It is, but remember it is thematically a book about the effect of the pure and fresh gospel when it makes its way into the spiritual digestive stream of an individual. Al Isaksen was that individual who became faithful on the delivery end as a pastor.

For now, though, I need to continue to build the personal case where the distinction was made between the authentic and the counterfeit. Pastor Al, the Milkman, was the former.

Back to Tennessee.

Stephen Gaskin was clearly the sole leader of the Farm. His teachings, compiled in the book *Monday Night Class*, became the mantra of the movement. Shortly before heading south on my solo journey, I read his book religiously. I had never before read any teachings that had the combined elements of philosophy, spirituality, and practicality. It became my Bible. Its pages became well worn.

Before I entered the Farm "town," I visited a few other communes, about which I had read and heard. At each one I would stay in my camper, unless I was invited in, but I would always eat and work with the folks at each commune. In those days, social life was a bit different. "Getting in people's faces" was not cool, whereas giving space was. In other words, don't ask questions, just "be."

So, I would observe others, but I acted like I didn't care what they were doing. No one seemed to notice me, but they did notice my truck and camper.

It was not really a camper. It was my home and my identity. I designed and built it with occasional help from my friends. This house on wheels was a mixture of lumber that I purchased and wood that I salvaged from a silo. Complex, curved, aerodynamic roofs defined the structure. On each side and on the back door were colored Plexiglas windows. Its curvature matched the rounded appearance of my rescued and restored 1952 sky-blue Chevy pickup that carried it. It was definitely art nouveau. When it was done, it looked like a church on wheels. It wasn't designed that way, but it certainly looked like it.

The truck with camper became my ticket in. Wherever I went, people thought it was cool, and therefore I must be cool as well. No one seemed to care enough to find out, though. I considered that odd at the time. I have learned since that man looks at the outward appearance and makes many assumptions by what he sees. There was nothing "cool" about me on the inside.

The experience at each commune was unique. I had no problem fitting into any of them, except for one. It was too academic, strict, and, in my observation, scary. They were experimenting with group parenting, and the children were at risk. Because all responsibilities were shared and I was accepted into the community, I was assigned as one duty to watch their babies, as they lay naked in their "perfect environment." It was a Plexiglas, temperature-controlled cube. They called it a Skinner Box, named after their "guru," psychologist B. F. Skinner. I could not help feeling sorry for these innocent children, growing up as if they were a lab experiment.

By now they have grown and are likely involved in education and politics, determining policies and our nation's future. If that is the case, their experiment has had questionable successes.

The place that had the greatest impact upon me was the Farm and its leader, Stephen Gaskin. It is important for me to note that until that time I had not met any of my "gurus" that had impressed me enough to make life changes. Not that I hadn't tried.

Bob Dylan was my first folk hero. In the early seventies I had managed to get an open invite to his house by a friend who lived in Woodstock and knew his housekeeper. Needless to say, I was awed by the opportunity, even though Dylan was not home. As much as I wanted to fully "dig" the experience, I got an unnerving feeling about the environment. It had a sense of being outside the natural realm, but I couldn't put my finger on what was wrong. Inside, the house was in great shape, decent and orderly. Photographs and artwork were thoughtfully placed. There was even a quote that Joan Baez had left on the blackboard. It was pretty flat though, and I remember wondering why it was left there. The driveway up to the house was long and wandered through the woods. As I looked out the window, I spotted a couple of photographers with telescopic lenses setting themselves up as if they were snipers looking for a dangerous criminal. I was told that they hang out in the woods waiting for someone famous to show up. It was their job. I wondered if they thought I was famous.

Hopefully, no one lost his or her job on my account.

Another time I was in Mill Valley, just outside of San Francisco, visiting some friends who had done the western migration trip in the late sixties. They had become familiar with many of the locals and where they hung out. One of them was Jerry Garcia, lead guitarist and vocalist for the Grateful Dead.

Garcia was my hero. I considered his music my heartbeat.

"If anyone knew where it was at," I thought, "it was Garcia." I was wrong.

It was a small café-like bar, where locals played and just sat around. That night there was only a handful of people. Apparently there were no drug laws in place, or else the police did not enforce them, because everyone did what they wanted without any paranoia. So we hung out and acted cool with my guru of rock and roll. My friend hinted to Jerry that I played the sax (I had started three months before) to see if he would ask me to jam with him after his break. He did not. That was fortunate for me. What was also fortunate was the experience to see him in that setting. What I left with was nothing. He was very quiet; in fact, he was silent. I don't recall him saying anything to anyone. It wasn't that he had this "heavy" meditative stare. He just seemed kind of blank, like there was no reason to engage anyone.

I want to make clear that this is no indictment against my "heroes," just an observation. They happened to be extremely talented people who were propped up to be more than who they were, as if they were gods. To many of us, regrettably, they were.

Out of all people in my miniature scope of influence, though, Stephen Gaskin was the one whom I had come to believe had "arrived."

When I set out to visit the Farm, it was more than simply my personal journey; my trip to Tennessee had a larger purpose. My hope was to meet with Stephen personally to share my vision so that I could start a Farm branch in the Northeast.

The Tennessee Farm was the mother of smaller start-ups in different states. My vision was to meet Stephen and get his approval and support to establish a Farm in New Jersey when I returned. Our specialization would be to design and build furniture, which would ensure our self-sufficiency. Staying outside the "system" was critical, and this was my ticket to do so. I was totally pumped to meet him, but to my great disappointment he was not there. He was in jail.

Tabernacle
on wheels

CHAPTER 12

...Still Looking

The Farm's public policy was that their community was drug free. That included marijuana. Apparently private policy was adjustable. It did not interest me to know the details of his sentence. When I heard about his absence, I was quite disappointed, for that was the main purpose of my visit. I wanted to see the Farm. Not only was its actual existence necessary for me to see, but also I had to meet its founder, Stephen Gaskin, the man whose teaching had become my life mantra. The community was built upon the lessons he taught.

It is important for me to point out that my understanding of world history left me without much hope for the future. It seemed to me that the centuries were filled with failure and futility. Not that I was fully versed in the affairs of man through the ages, but what I had learned left me feeling like the prospect of the future was dismal. I wanted successful community. Why, I did not know, but I felt it was part of my design and I did not think I was alone.

As a child, my favorite times were when my relatives came to visit us or when we went to their homes. There, the aunts and uncles would talk and laugh and the cousins would play. Departure time always came too soon. Then everything would change. Adults would go back to work, children would return to school, and no one seemed to be happy. Could there not be a way to capture and preserve what we were so limited to experience?

When I started to explore communal living through books and personal visits, I learned a frightening lesson: most attempts were failures. The ones that were considered to be successful as a commune or community fit into one of two categories: either it had a very strong and charismatic leader, or it had a strong economic and religious bond. The main criterion for success was longevity. If this were true, then the odds were slim. Why did my heart long for something that seemed so distant, so difficult to attain? Was I indeed a dreamer, or was there something real that I hoped for, something that had yet to materialize? After many miles of travel and various stays in communes along my way, my heart was still unsettled. I set my sights on the Farm as the place, and Stephen Gaskin as the one who could reach my high expectations.

It did not happen.

To my surprise, Stephen returned while I was still there. The atmosphere was alive with expectancy. We did get to meet, but something completely unexpected happened to me. Call it Providence or coincidence, but no sooner did we meet, than it all came apart—literally. You see, the Farm diet is completely centered on soybeans. They grow and process them into every form imaginable. This was new to my diet, especially the quantity, and at the moment I met Stephen, my body began its rebellion.

I wasn't sure if it was cool to excuse myself, but I had no time to find out. I had to run. Never before had I imagined that a bean could be that powerful of a motivational force.

After running like a kid in a three-legged potato sack race to the nearest outhouse, I found relief enough to return and find Stephen in a nearby field. I was able to continue our brief conversation, but immediately realized that my time was short.

I got to the point about wanting to start a division of the Farm in New Jersey, and he was all for it. "Go for it, man," he said.

That was the last thing he said, and I took him literally.

I went for it—the outhouse, that is. When I returned, he was no longer around. I was told later that, as part of his sentence, he was given freedom to return to the Farm on weekends.

Soon I was leaving the Farm, impressed by the operation but still empty from what I felt was missing. On my way out I picked up a hitchhiker. He told me that he was one of the original residents. He looked it.

I asked him some questions, but he sounded somewhat disenchanted. He told me Stephen was part of a group marriage. Only those who had reached a certain aura were permitted to do so, but not the entire community. I had no accurate way to validate what he said, but I had no reason to disbelieve him. I was not surprised, but I was very disappointed.

Even though I prided myself in a culture with limited moral constraint, something inside of me said this sanction was absolutely wrong. I was somewhat shocked at myself. What I would have previously considered to be Victorian thinking was now originating from my own head, and I had no argument!

I started to think about loyalty and devotion. If that is missing from human relations, then our lives are reduced to a "one-night stand."

I continued my travels farther south, but my utopian hopes were rapidly losing weight. The next hitchhikers that I stopped for did nothing to console me.

They both looked beat up and barely made it into the truck. They were two hippies who had been spending their time "truckin'" from city to city, sleeping in parks and sharing the message of love, peace, and happiness. But that chapter had come to a close for this duo.

The previous night they were robbed and beaten by a few of their own, who had apparently gotten hold of some "bad psychedelics" and took it out on them. They said things are not like they used to be. I suppose Dylan was right when he sang, "These times, they are a-changin'." The problem for me was that they were changing a bit too rapidly. This movement was barely a decade in process. Was this "Woodstock Nation" that I was longing for really just a pipe dream? "Where had all the flowers gone?"

I landed in Fort Lauderdale, party central of eastern winters, but that was of no interest to me. The direction I was traveling in my journey to find substance in this life was shifting its course without my recognition.

I ran out of money. If I was to continue my journey, I needed a job. I got one in a plastic furniture shop. That was odd and in radical contrast to the life I was pursuing—definitely not organic. What was even stranger to me was my nightlife. It became nonexistent.

My only interest was to retire to my truck and read the Bible. The Bible!

That was something that I never had done before. The only reason I had one was because a friend's mother had given it to me a few years before. I carried it with me on my "holy" shelf that had the *Bhagavad Gita*, *The Teachings of the Compassionate Buddha*, and the Tao teachings of Lao Tzu and Chuang Tzu. Until that time, my only literary interest was Stephen

Gaskin's *Monday Night Class* or Baba Ram Dass's book, titled
Be Here Now.

My attraction to the Bible was new and unusual. I felt compelled to read it. It was not that I understood what I was reading. I did not. I found it interesting, but I felt like a stranger
looking through the window of someone else's home. Nevertheless, I read.

A new thought began to develop in me, the thought of marriage. Marla and I had been together for about five years, and
I had not considered it. I began to feel very wrong about that.
Although I loved her and felt fully connected to her, I offered
her no signs of commitment. I assumed she knew that I was
committed, even though my lifestyle brought her no sense of
security. I began to see myself from her eyes and did not like
what I saw. I was more like the proverbial "Wandering Jew," not
a future husband. That was soon to change.

Marla was able to save up enough money to fly down to see me.

As soon as I saw her I realized she meant more to me than I
ever considered. I loved her, and I wanted to spend my future
with her. That much became very clear. In my awkward form
of proposing, I suggested we get married. She was shocked to
hear those words from my mouth, and she took it to be my
proposal, which it was.

She went north—elated. Soon afterward, I returned to
New Jersey, and we moved to a rental house in the country
with another couple. In June of 1976, in our backyard, we had
our wedding.

My close friend Alex was the likely candidate to perform the
vows. He and I had grown up together since the early sixties. He
also knew Marla very well. The only issue was his latest fanat-

icism. He was a born-again Christian, actually the first I had ever met. He became one while he and I were living in a rented farmhouse a few towns away. Since then he had gone to Bible school, which made him official in my eyes. All we needed was a local magistrate present to make it legal. Somehow we found one, and he became our lawful witness to our very different sort of wedding day.

My mother was extremely excited that I had awakened from my fantasy world and was planning to wed. Her only stipulation concerned Alex. He was the one Gentile friend of mine that she actually liked, but she had one clear condition. If he were to mention Jesus at the ceremony, she would not attend. That was no problem with me. At that point of my journey, Jesus was all right with me, but as the Doobie Brothers lyrics went, Jesus was "*just* all right." I certainly found no connection between Jesus and me. When I told Alex about my mother's concern, he agreed not to say His name. What I have learned since then is that Alex may not have mentioned His name, but whatever he did, he did *in* His name.

I have since shared publicly the story of our wedding day, and some have said it should be published or at least become a scene in a movie, but that will have to wait. On June 5, 1976, we became man and wife and have been married ever since.

Good job, Alex. Better job, Jesus.

Our lives were now connected, and my journey was seriously altered in a way I had never dreamed possible.

Within three years, we were moving back to the suburbs of Long Island with our first child, a beautiful girl we named Brook. We purchased a small bungalow that was in need of much work. The down payment was $650, but it still took me six months to save for it. My plan was to fix it up and sell it in one year. Then we would move back to the country to begin our life of self-sufficiency. My vision had not changed; it was just extended. From now on it would include my wife and daughter. In my heart, I was still a hippie, and I felt extremely out of place in the suburbs, a setting to which I promised myself I would never return.

One morning I was sipping coffee and looking out my kitchen window at the neighborhood kids playing in our yard. Our property was all front yard with big old trees. Before we moved there, the house was abandoned, so it became the neighborhood park for the kids on our block. At that time, it was the best thing about living there. Watching the kids helped me to forget all the airplanes, which constantly flew above us, and the traffic, which awaited me each morning on my way to work.

This morning was different. As I gazed through the lens of my coffee cup, my attention was seized by Winter. She was the eldest daughter of our next-door neighbor, Sharon. At the time, she was about twelve or thirteen and full of life. She radiated joy and set the tone for the other kids. She was probably the happiest girl of that age I had ever met. My problem was that she had no reason to be so. Her mother had moved them back to Long Island from Colorado in order to get away from an abusive husband and father. They lived in a tiny, shack-like house. Sharon cleaned homes and did other odd jobs to keep them going. She was a woman who was content, even though she had every reason not to be. She told us that shortly after moving to Long Island she met Jesus and became born again. I still did not get what that meant, but that morning my interest was piqued. It had to do with Winter's shirt.

As I watched them run around and play, I was so fixed on her laughter and enthusiasm that I missed the message stitched above her heart. Once I focused on those words, everything would begin to change.

"Praise the Lord," it read.

I put down my cup, and without another thought I ran outside. I called Winter to me and asked her what it meant.

She said it was about Jesus and how good He was all the time. Then she was off again.

I have thought about that brief conversation many times since then. It literally took about seven seconds, but it propelled me into an entirely new journey.

Maybe my entire search was based on my limited thinking. Could it have been that there was something I was missing? Was there another path to consider?

Paul's new address: "on the road"

CHAPTER 13

Freedom

*"He has made everything beautiful in its time.
Also, He has put eternity into man's heart..."*
Ecclesiastes 3:11, ESV

It wasn't more than two weeks before my Communist boss let it all loose. It was lunchtime, and the crew was eating in the basement of another million-dollar house. As usual, I ate alone because the conversations were pitiful at best. This noon hour took the Emmy.

My boss and the builder began an unusual conversation. It was not long before I realized it was for my benefit.

"Hitler was a smart man," the builder said.

Did I hear him right?

"Hitler was a fool," countered my boss. This was getting interesting. That was one of the smartest things I had heard my boss say.

"If he were smart, he would have finished the job and killed them all."

At that moment something went off inside of me. It was as if every swastika in every bathroom I had ever seen had been posted by my boss. Every slur that read "Kill the Jews" had been in his handwriting. In my mind, he became responsible for every offense against my people for all time. My heart was filled with vengeance, and I could not sit still. I devised a plan in a split second. There were two shovels leaning against the concrete wall. With one I would kill my boss. It had to be swift and hard because he was built like a tractor. The other would be for the builder. He deserved the same. I was about to get up without another thought when I heard his familiar, angry voice.

"Get up and get back to work!"

I knew it was too late. I was defeated without one step.

On the way home that day I was filled with sorrow. Not only had another plan of mine failed, but what I experienced in my heart was so dark. In one moment I committed a double homicide. How could I, this self-proclaimed citizen of Woodstock Nation, whose constitution was all about love, peace, and happiness, commit an act of horror like I did in that basement? I knew I did it. It was as clear as anything else I had ever done. I had even read the words of Jesus not long before that said if I harbored hatred in my heart, I was guilty of murder.

In my mind I was guilty of murder, hypocrisy, and a host of other offenses that I could not bear. It was a hard ride home.

My infected finger compounded the pain. An unhealed wound had swollen so large that I cringed when it was brushed against. I was no stranger to infection; it seemed I was prone to it. Twice I was hospitalized: once for gangrene, and another time when I was placed in isolation for a severe cellulitis. This pain was worse, though, and my boss never let me tend to it. We had no insurance, nor could I afford to take time off to have it looked at. We lived hand-to-mouth, and I needed to keep working. When I got home, I told Marla about my finger but nothing about the incident. I thought I would have to go to the emergency room and have it cut off.

Marla had a different idea.

"Why don't you pray to Jesus to heal it?"

It was so strange to hear that from her, but it made sense. Our next-door neighbors prayed to Jesus for everything: their food, their gasoline—they even prayed for their dog and cat, and they always got what they needed. I had nothing to lose.

But pray? That was not something I did. The only praying I knew was in Hebrew. The only place I ever did it was in the synagogue, what we called Temple. Our house had nothing holy about it. It was old and in need of help. I had stripped the walls so I could insulate them. But this was where I lived, and now was when I needed help.

I slumped down on the kitchen floor with my back against a stud and began a conversation—a desperate one.

"God, I don't even know if you are real. Jesus, I don't know who you are. But I need help, and I am helpless. If you are God, please help me."

I forgot all about my finger. It took second place to the pain within my heart. I do not know how long I sat there, but I know that tears began to stream down my face, something that had not happened before in my memory. The next sound I heard was Marla's voice.

"Look at your finger!"

I looked down at my hand and saw my finger oozing ugliness. I had tried soaking it for days in hot salty water but to no avail. Now the infection was flowing steadily from it. I noticed something else, though, and that was my heart. It was lighter. The pain and the disease that had plagued it were also gone. I felt unusually good. Gladness, which had become so foreign, now came over me. The next morning I awoke, afraid that it was not real. But it was. Not only was my infection gone, but my finger looked like the infection had never existed.

What was even better was my life.

It was new. I was excited about the day and what it had in store. I felt like I was "born again," even though I had never been told it. Not long after that day, I would read John chapter three and know exactly what Jesus was talking about.

I went back to work that day a new man. I was eager to work.

However, I faced the same boss. Looking back, I think he did not expect to see me. The first thing he told me that morning was that if I wanted to keep my job, I would have to take a one-dollar cut in pay per hour. I told him I was worth more, not less, and that was unacceptable. I was surprised at my new boldness. He gave me five days to think about it. I knew that if he fired me, like he had so many others, he would be liable to pay unemployment insurance, another thing for which he detested America. For the next five days, he would attempt to get me to quit. It did not work.

Day after day he would have me do dangerous and highly strenuous jobs to force my hand. On the last day he singled me out to go with him. We were going to dig holes for a pole barn.

I followed him to the house where a state supreme court judge lived. It was a a gorgeous location, a part of Long Island that I never knew.

We strung out the row of poles and he handed me my posthole digger. I would start on one end and he the other. I assumed he thought he would either work me to death or bury me here. I started digging. I was actually enjoying myself. I felt a new strength. I realized that I was no longer working for him but for

Jesus, my Deliverer. That became more evident as the day went on. It was a long line, but I noticed he was having some trouble.

He kept swatting the air. As I got closer with every completed hole, I saw his problem. He had a swarm of gnats around his head. I didn't.

I kept digging. I don't remember stopping for lunch. Maybe we did. I do remember finally meeting him mid-row. (I actually think I did more than he did, but I want to err on the conservative.) I put my shovel and bar in his truck, and he gave me my check. It was a liberating moment, and I walked away, refraining myself from skipping and jumping. I heard his voice one last time.

"You will never make it as a carpenter."

For the first time in my new life, God spoke to me: "That is the voice of your adversary, the devil, not the voice of Truth. Recognize it, but never listen to it again."

On the way home I felt so free. No job, but real freedom. I realized that my ex-boss was like the Pharaoh in Egypt. I was like a slave and Jesus was my Moses. Even the swarm of gnats played their role in my new story. The Bible that day became a living document. I was no longer a slave. I was part of the redemption story.

Something new and exciting began. It didn't seem to matter to me that I was jobless. A sense of anticipation developed with this new friendship. Jesus had become my friend and everything seemed okay!

Within a few months of my experience, our second daughter, Rachel, was born, and my wife was born again. Our life of trusting God together had now begun.

CHAPTER 14

"I Will Build My Church"

In many ways the journey had just begun. A new desire was born in our hearts. However, we lacked companions who were like-minded, those who had experienced a life conversion, a newfound faith, and a living way. We knew it had to be centered upon Jesus because He was the pioneer of our faith. But we had no positive connotation of church. We somehow knew that there must be a congregation of those, like us, called out of the wilderness of uncertainty. Like migrating birds we sought out a flock with which we could fly. Maybe it was spiritual instinct, but we sensed there must be people like us who gather in community to share this freedom, which was so new and alive. From what we had understood of church, though, it had to be found elsewhere. We were both right and wrong.

Gospel Community was the second church we visited. The first one was filled with young people and good music. By all appearances we fit right in, but something did not feel right.

When the pastor arose to speak, I discovered what it was that I was feeling.

"The Lord spoke to me while we were in worship, that at 10:45 we are to lock the doors," he said. "God wants His people to be on time."

Who was I, a complete novice, to question this man who spoke with such authority. Yet I could not ignore what I was thinking.

What if our neighbor Sharon was on her way here with her three children, and one of her tread-less tires decided it had gone far enough. Would God send an angel to change it so she and her family would not be locked out? If this was the pastor's picture of God, and this truly was a voice he had heard, then I must politely excuse myself, even though I do not think that *polite* was how I was feeling. Besides, how did he know that God was speaking?

So with our first visit came our first disappointment.

Perhaps this is why I am compelled to write this journal.

I have since encountered hundreds of disappointed and dis-illusioned and even disgusted sojourners since that day, and many have given up on the notion of church in America today. In fact, we are losing an entire generation of perceptive youth, who see church as a manufactured gathering of older folks who gather on Sunday mornings. They come because of their insecurity or their lives are so dull that they have nothing else to do.

But Jesus said, "I will build My church."

At the time I met Jesus I was fully into building. Design and structure were my passions. I studied those who did it well. I wanted what they had.

Until I met Jesus.

He took my passion to an entirely new dimension. I knew that He was to be studied and followed. My path had dead-ended. It was heading to a precipice. Like any other life, at that point in the road, Jesus stood on the edge. With His scarred, outstretched hands, He stood as if to say, "You need not go any farther."

Jesus always spoke the truth and did what He said He would do. He said He would build and He has been building ever since. His structure is strong, eternally so, and it is beautiful.

Because I have experienced His life as real, I am compelled to write about it. The sad reality in most of America is that what we call church is something else. No one issued a permit for the "building" that so lifelessly continues to gather in churches Sunday after Sunday. What should be a weekly family reunion of freed slaves is typically just another day in an already over-scheduled life. This is also why I am writing about Al Isaksen, the milkman who became my pastor.

Pastor Al allowed Jesus to build and build and build without getting in His way. If that was his only gift, it was enough to bring continuity to the message first delivered to our forefathers on the day of Jesus' ascension.

But there was more.

As with any good building, it could be no stronger than its members, and it lacked beauty if pieces were placed where they did not belong.

Those who had the opportunity to sit under the Milkman's ministry experienced the life of Jesus displayed in genuine love and humility. Acceptance was the initial step. Man looks at the outward appearance; we all know that. Madison Avenue has thrived because of that. We want to look good to be accepted.

That can be rather expensive.

Pastor Al accepted everyone, regardless of how they looked or how they dressed. He allowed the God Who looks at the heart to see people through his eyes.

Once accepted, those people become accessible. They are more likely to let down their guards and be themselves. That is when Jesus, the Builder, can begin shaping that individual as a vital part of His building.

There was a time when young people began showing up at the church door with long hair, beards, leather jackets, and no shoes. There were those who thought Pastor Al should address the way people come to church. His advice in return was to let God dictate the dress. If He entered the inside of a person to make him a new creation, it would show up eventually on the outside. How can a person understand the inner work of the Holy Spirit if he is caught up on managing another's outward appearance? When an unkempt person reads in the Bible that, as a believer, his body becomes the temple of the Holy Spirit, he becomes convinced that some change needs to occur. Renovation begins. The structure is altered on the inside, and the outward appearance follows, if indeed there is need of that.

There was also another unusual aspect of Pastor Al's leadership: that was the depth of love he had for those who came to know him. He became your best friend. In fact, many have testified of being Pastor Al's closest friend. That almost sounds manipulative, but consider Jesus.

As your relationship develops with Him, Jesus becomes your closest friend. Pastor Al simply modeled that pattern. It became natural to him. Who would not feel especially loved by someone who was genuinely interested in who you are? It did not take long for people who truly wanted a deeper understanding of Jesus to spend more time with Pastor Al.

It was his model of discipleship, and it was successful.

As a result, many ministries are still vibrantly preaching and teaching the same gospel that quickens the heart toward righteousness and purposeful living.

Today there is a retreat center in upstate New York that bears witness to that style of ministry. It began as a place where the elderly, the bruised, and the vulnerable could spend time in a safe environment. A family, devoted to serve others as they bore daily witness to the presence of Jesus in their lives, ran it. On weekends the retreat center became a place where believers could gather and experience intimate, spiritual, worshipful life that everyday routine often crowds out. It was named Shiloh, which means "deep peace." Shiloh was a city in Israel, where the Ark of the Covenant was stationed for centuries. In the Old Testament, the Ark was always the representation of the presence of God. It is also a prophetic name for the coming Messiah.

Only heaven can register the effect of the lives restored and ministries begun through time spent at Shiloh because of the presence of God abiding on that piece of real estate. It was not magical; it was developed by faith through the leading of God's Spirit and the many men and women who came alongside to sacrificially participate in designing, building, and maintaining what was originally a vision in Pastor Al's mind.

That is what proper spiritual leadership can accomplish.

"Land that drinks in the rain often falling on it and that produces a crop useful to those for whom it is farmed receives the blessing of God" (Hebrews 6:7, NIV).

There are probably over a dozen churches and ministries that sprang out of the little old church on Atlantic Avenue. They sprang up naturally from men and women who sat under the Milkman's ministry. Pastor Al did not have a huge vision for the future. There were no vision-casting meetings, no five- or ten-year plans. Organizations do that, not organisms. He read from the scriptures that men who have been made faithful are to teach men to be faithful. In that process, he made room for opportunity to exercise men of faith in their gifting. How God called them into position was His business. Pastor Al did not interfere in the building process. Like Nehemiah, he stationed himself with a trowel in one hand and a sword in the other, working on his portion of "Jerusalem's wall." He was always in awe of how God could start with a mess and build a masterpiece.

CHAPTER 15

At His Table

Pastor Al made a huge difference in my life. I say *made* because his days on earth are now passed. Memories of him, though, will continue to shape me. We were an unlikely duo, he and I—generation gap, cultural divide, Jew and Gentile—yet we became friends, an act that happens in few instances apart from Jesus. He makes the two one and breaks the dividing walls of hostility in every shape and size.

However, it was easy to make friends with Al Isaksen and I am far from alone in that experience. He made himself accessible. In fact I doubt that he kept an appointment book. People seemed to just drop in for a visit.

I love to recall the many times I would pull up the narrow driveway that separated the church from their home and drop in unannounced. I would knock first, but if no one answered, the known custom was to walk in. I can still hear the creak of that wooden storm door when it would slowly close behind me as I took the two steps across their back porch to the kitchen door. I would offer another short knock before poking my head in for a subdued shout. Before long Pastor Al would respond, "Praise the Lord!" His voice always greeted like a melody.

"Good to see you, Paul," he'd say as he reached out his long slender arms to welcome me. I immediately felt at home. He always greeted with a huge unpretentious smile. It was as if he was not only waiting for my arrival, but he was anticipating it. Yet he did not know that I was coming. Or did he?

Before long he or Dorothy would put on a pot of fresh coffee and offer something to eat. However eager he was to know why I had come, he never pried. When you entered through that door and sat at that kitchen table, you were treated as a sojourner in need of refreshing. His table became a sanctuary, a place of refuge where baggage could be dropped. I suppose if one were interested in talking baseball, he would provide the listening ear, but before long he would get to the heart of the visit.

"So what has the Lord been saying to you lately, Paul?"

He truly wanted to know. In fact, that was his counseling technique, although he never considered himself a counselor, nor had he received any formal training to be one. He was well acquainted with the Word of God, though, and trusted in the God of the Word to release its power in any situation.

"Counsel lies deep within the heart of man, and a man of understanding draws it out," the Proverbs say.

He never said this was his technique, nor had I heard him reference it, but I have seen its result in dozens of people who merely took the time to sit with him and talk, many around this same table. It was his greatest form of ministry.

"Naturally supernatural."

That was his favorite description of the Christian life. It was naturally supernatural. He believed that when a person came to faith in the Messiah, the truth of God would begin its work of transformation. Reality was never denied, simply put in position as a lesser truth.

To Pastor Al, when Jesus was enthroned in a person's heart, He became their righteousness, and they became the dwelling place of His Holy Spirit. From within, God's truth could begin the process of freedom and transformation. Yes, problems were real and at times overwhelming, but in the process of time, the Deliverer would complete the work of sanctification that began at the cross.

When a believer sat at Al's table, he was appreciated as an object of God's affection and a subject of God's attention. Pastor Al felt it his calling to allow God to see through his eyes and hear through his ears. No one was simply a subject of pastoral ministry on his day timer.

Perhaps that is what made him so unique.

He believed.

He believed what the Bible said. He accepted it as truth and experienced it as dependable. As a result he saw great potential sitting across the table from him, and great value as well. Each one was both a target of God's love and a vessel into which His nature was being formed. He took joy and privilege in simply becoming better acquainted with each visitor. Time spent with him was uplifting and His love for God was contagious. It never failed. Inevitably I would leave my visit wanting to know this Jesus more than I did when I came. My love and devotion for Him grew with each visit.

"To know Him is to love Him, and to love Him is to serve Him."

I wonder how many people left that kitchen with renewed zeal and affirmation.

I can count at least six pastors who began their journey at that table, and several others who are deeply involved in various forms of ministry. I have since discovered that fellowship amongst believers was that refreshing, just like a glass of milk is to an Oreo cookie. In fact that was the basis of his discipleship and counseling. He would call it weak, I would call it effective. When a person came in laden down with troubles and sensed the presence of Jesus, life had a tendency of finding a new perspective. This truth became personal to me in 1984.

Marla and I, along with our two little girls, had moved to Chicago so that I could attend Bible College. I had sensed a calling to understand more fully the Book that I had come to believe. If I were to invest my life in its teachings and bring up our children under its authority, I had to become far more literate. I needed clear, concise, and thorough instruction on the Bible's origins, authenticity, and inerrancy—as well as a deeper understanding of the history that surrounded its era. I needed to be separated from routine and able to concentrate on study like never before. I felt the need to be immersed in its teachings by those who staked their own lives on its validity.

The move was not without great difficulty.

My life soon became engrossed in school and study. Saturdays and any other available time were dedicated to earning a living. The only financial support we had was from an older couple that sent us thirty-five dollars a month. I never asked for any. If this was God, He would also have to provide. Not long after our move, I began to renovate our kitchen in return for our rent—a very messy job to live amidst. I soon became sick with multiple infections, none of which were fully diagnosed until shortly before our move back to New York over a year and a half later. My energy level was depleted and I had little to give to family life. They suffered as a result. The girls were resilient and they had each other. Marla, on the other hand, bore the burden of my absence and involvement.

Living at the poverty level in a strange city without the security of home, friends, and a strong church family became too much for her. The pressures began to mount and she faced great difficulty in coping with daily life. On top of that, we had two attempted break-ins, more than half of my income-producing tools stolen from the storage space the landlord provided, a car that continuously broke down, an apartment that was plagued by roaches and my life seriously threatened by a raging man who lived above us. When he attempted to kick in our solid oak door and failed, I was convinced it was time to move. Our new friends had an apartment above a funeral home, where the four of us moved into and slept in one tiny bedroom.

Did I mention that the sun barely shined in Chicago? It seemed like it would try, but then the wind would blow it away.

Life was somewhat gray, especially for Marla. In my busyness, I missed the mounting turmoil until it became inescapable. She felt very alone.

Was not God there?

Yes, He was.

Did He not care?

Yes, He did.

Could He not bring deliverance?

Not only did He, but if He had not, I would have nothing to write about.

That deliverance was through a process, which became my most important lesson.

One of the reasons I am writing this story about Pastor Al, the Milkman, is because his life was an example of how naturally God can work the supernatural into our lives and be a very present help in time of trouble. But as I witnessed the deepening need for God's presence and purpose to be made known to Marla, I also sensed my own inadequacy to help. It was not that I didn't try, nor was I lacking tears as I cried out to God from the depths of my being. I just felt so limited in knowledge and I second-guessed why I was putting my family through such havoc for my own selfish desire. How could God ordain anything with this kind of outcome?

The process I spoke of was more one of elimination than one of clear guidance. It became the strongest lesson of the value of Pastor Al's ministry and the effectiveness and simplicity of the gospel when it is naturally worked out.

The Bible says that the power of God is not released by the cunning craftiness of human wisdom, but its demonstration is displayed through those who live by faith in the abiding nature of the Spirit of Jesus. The Milkman lived this out...but I am getting ahead of myself.

I began to reason that I was a third-semester student in an advanced study program that was in its final months. Surely in this large and renowned institution I should be able to locate some wise and experienced counsel that could "fix" my wife and restore my family. Until that time we had never settled into a church fellowship. It was not that we did not try; we just never felt any place was home. We tried various parts of the city and still came up short, always leaving empty. It wasn't that the gospel wasn't preached, or worship skillfully displayed, but mostly because we never experienced the warmth of Christian fellowship to which we were so accustomed at Gospel Community.

"Do me a favor," Pastor Al would often say at the close of an evening service. "Look around and see if there is anyone you don't know and ask him or her to join you in the back for a cup of coffee." It was by no means a social club, but the atmosphere was cultivated for newcomers to feel welcomed, loved, and accepted. The warmth of Christian love was the norm.

Why was this so hard to discover in this so-called evangelical city? At least that was my experience. What I did find were very well-polished alumni with excellent backgrounds in Greek and Hebrew, as well as extensive historical context in their biblical exegeses and expositions. Tight delivery and stirring messages were prevalent, but what mattered to us most was painfully missing.

Where was this Jesus Whom they preached? Did He not promise to be where two or more were gathered in His Name? Why did we not experience the atmosphere that surrounded Jesus' earthly visit? What happened to the personal intimacy that characterized His ministry? They taught that miracles were not for today, but what about setting the captives free, loosing the oppressed, the love for the brethren and concern for the stranger? Was I expecting too much? Was I getting too personal?

It came to the point where Marla no longer wanted to continue our Sunday morning ritual of expectation and disappointment. I was not about to give up because I felt too much was at stake. I took the girls with me, determined that we would find a church where Jesus would be.

I came up empty. I resigned myself—that instead of looking for Jesus to meet me, I would bring Him to meet others. The girls and I began taking a Sunday morning walk to a local nursing home in a Jewish section of the city. They loved the girls, but after a few weeks they gave me a not-so-fond farewell for sharing the gospel with one patient in particular. It grieved me. Not only was she missing both arms and legs because of acute diabetes, but she refused my message because of the long dark history it had with her ancestors.

Paving my way into the nursing home was in part to make a way for our family to share in ministry. My hope was to restore my wife's perspective. Hope was beginning to wane. I sought counsel.

I visited the VP of the Bible college. He was a man whom I highly respected. I shared our situation as he listened intently. In response he told me about his troubled teenage son and how his behavior had greatly affected his wife's psychological well-being. He sent her to a counselor and suggested I consider the same. I was stunned. I was not looking for professional help—I was seeking godly counsel.

Apparently he sensed my apprehension, but he misread it.

He then told me that the school had a fund for married students and that they could pay for my first visit. He assured me that I had nothing to lose. I was not at all convinced, but out of confusion I agreed to try. Even though I wanted to believe there was another way, I began to second-guess myself because of my failed attempts.

That night I did my best to persuade Marla that this would be a new beginning and hope was on the horizon. She had little strength to argue and submitted to my decision. So I took a day off from school and we drove north into the suburbs to a well-furnished and decorated counselor's office. In the waiting room I searched for evidence of Jesus' presence but found none, not a plaque or even a magazine article. I waited somewhat nervously while Marla was called in. I prayed, still wondering if this was the right move. One of the names of Jesus in prophecy is "Wonderful Counselor." Perhaps this man was a member of that ministry.

Perhaps not.

It was not long before my wife came through the door, far more upset than when she entered. She made it clear that she wanted nothing more to do with his counsel. He soon followed to talk more, but she was done and left for the car. He said we had one more half hour of paid time and that I should take advantage of it. I was somewhat shocked, but in my patience I preserved my soul and heard him out.

In few minutes of listening my patience was gone. I'd heard enough. His counsel was for her to return for more counsel. He spoke without compassion, like a scientist after a failed experiment. I asked him if he was a Christian. He said he was. I asked him, why then did he not speak that way. Why did he not speak out of a heart that weeps for the brokenness of humanity, rather than one who preys upon the pain of the wounded?

He listened to me because I had paid the fare up front—not because he cared. I wanted to turn the tables over, but instead I walked out in disgust, feeling like I had failed to protect my wife from this wolf.

It was a long ride back to the apartment.

I am not sure how long afterward, but I received a call from Pastor Al. He asked about Marla. I told him she was hurting. Without asking too many questions, he suggested she come home for a visit. She could stay with them.

"She probably just needs a time of refreshing." It was the first assuring words I had heard in a long time.

Before long she was boarding a plane to New York. Someone, to whom I remain grateful, paid her fare. Marla was hesitant to leave the girls and me behind, but I assured her it would be short and we would be fine.

One week later the girls and I were at O'Hare International Airport awaiting Marla's return. In those days the expectant greeters would wait at the gate where the plane arrived. She came off the plane as if she had arrived from another planet. Her face glowed and she was jubilant.

"They looked to Him and were radiant, and their faces will never be ashamed" (Psalm 34:5, NAS).

After we settled our girls in bed that night, I quizzed Marla about Pastor Al's ministry. I wanted to know how he had counseled her. I knew there was no silver bullet, but he must have had some great insight because she was a different woman from a week ago. What I soon learned was that there was no counsel, at least nothing formal. However, the Counselor was there. Through Pastor Al, His presence was inescapable, simply by way of his sincere devotion to Him. As a milkman he would always deliver on time. As a milkman of a higher calling, he still delivered, and the timing was impeccable. He delivered the Gospel of God. It was and still is one of assurance, that the Jesus Who saves is the One Who delivers. He is a very present help in time of trouble. No one prescribes his need and no one determines the time. But in Jesus, the Messiah, we are not like those who grope in the darkness.

His product is always redemptive, but like fresh milk, it often requires a delivery. It is mysterious how that happens, but what is certain was in that week the truth was delivered, and that truth brought freedom in such a way that the supernatural seemed so natural.

"In the beginning was the Word, and the Word was with God, and the Word was God" (John 1:1, KJV).

"And the Word became flesh, and dwelt amongst us" (John 1:14, ASV).

Contrary to the teaching and practice of modern Christianity, the message of hope and freedom is not reserved for Sunday morning by the preacher or Monday through Friday in a professional counselor's office. (I suppose God takes Saturday off.)

His word is moved from one vessel to another through faith. True faith is rooted in the Word of God and released by those who believe. It becomes alive when any individual is open and willing to exchange his pride for God's assistance. Pastor Al became an expert at delivering the message of the gospel. As a milkman he would start his day at the source, filling his truck for the needs of his customers. His job was to deliver.

As a pastor his day began much the same, but from a new Source. This time, though, his product was alive and it "dwelt among us." It was no longer a mechanical fill-up at the loading dock each morning; it was a greeting and a conversation with the One Who delivered him and filled him with a life-giving message. It was delivered faithfully on Sunday mornings, as well as other scheduled times, but in no way was it limited to an itinerary.

As I continued to probe about the source and cause for my wife's turnabout, I was like a ready student, eager to take notes. What I discovered made my pen to drop and my eyes to open. It is a lesson that I have never forgotten, but I have yet to master. It is the lesson that requires faith, perhaps more than any other.

That is the lesson of the "naturally supernatural."

It is the inherent message of the gospel. It is widely accepted that God visited the earth in a manger on Christmas morning. The reason why is often short-circuited. It is an invisible message because it lodges in the spirits of redeemed men and women. In brief, it goes like this:

"…we have this treasure in earthen vessels."

"…Christ in you, the hope of glory."

"…as He (Jesus) is, so are we in this world."

These are the messages specifically given to the early believers after the death and resurrection of Jesus. These were given to explain what had happened to them. They were transformed from fearful fishermen and friends to waking warriors for the One Who freed them on the cross. Faith was no longer a lesson to learn, but it was life to live by.

The radical news of the gospel is that God is not religious. Not only did He not start a new religion, He came to abolish religion. I know that puts some on edge, so let me explain.

It is a quiet revolution that takes place in His followers. It requires no membership, no training and no privileged heritage. It crosses all borders of culture and race. "All you need is faith… just get on board"—faith of the Messiah that brings faith *in* the Messiah, Jesus. Once faith is poured into that earthen vessel, its purpose changes as does its direction. It is heading upward but reaching outward to capture as many passengers on board as possible. Those who respond to Jesus receive power and become willing to do God's will above any other. That is what grace does.

When Moses was confronted by the voice of God in the midst of a burning bush, he asked, "Whom shall I say sent me?"

God answered him, "Tell them *I AM* sent you."

Centuries later when Jesus stood before His accusers He identified Himself as the "*I AM.*"

When a person becomes a believer in Jesus, that same presence inhabits his earthly body. The body becomes a temple for the Holy Spirit of God. As a result, God is able to access individuals with whom that person relates. The New Testament calls it a mystery. Pastor Al had a firm grasp on it and discovered its simplicity.

Because this truth had made its home within him, he responded with hospitality. Just as one opens his house for visitors, he opened his life for those he encountered so that they too could meet Jesus. He acknowledged that his effectiveness was rooted in God's presence. Think of "presence" as a conjunction of "present tense." In reality, to miss His nearness at any time is to dismiss the available power we have through faith.

Pastor Al's greatest joy was to witness the freedom that occurred when the "I AM" was released through him. He took no recognition for the results. He was a vessel with a handle. He simply allowed God His firm grip. Like many of the routines of life, it became natural to him. At the same time, it was anything but natural.

It was divine—that is "naturally supernatural."

Very simply put, the liberating message of Jesus of Nazareth was designed for delivery through ordinary folks who have been delivered by it. Whether it is in a one-on-one setting or one-to-one-thousand, Jesus, Who promises to be present, shows up. As the Chambers Brothers song continues, "You don't need no ticket, you just thank the Lord."

Faith was always on the menu in Dorothy's kitchen when one sat with Pastor Al at his table.

When my wife spent a week in their home, she did not go through extensive counseling. She simply visited.

In an unpretentious environment, with whom the world would dismiss as an uneducated, simple man, power was released in an atmosphere of faith, and all the complexities of her life began to unwind.

"In Your presence there is fullness of joy" (Psalm 16:11, NAS)

That is how it happened at Pastor Al's table. As a milkman, he knew the healthy benefit of delivering his product in a timely fashion. He just left it at the door. As a pastor, he treated the gospel in the same manner. If any believer allows God access into the routines of life, His presence will assure healthy results within a world scrambling for solutions. Not only was his message refreshing, but through its delivery it brought deliverance.

While Marla was in Long Island, her brother came to visit her. Without prior knowledge, she discovered that he was going through a heartbreaking experience. His pain seemed incurable to him. Marla happened to be in Pastor Al's study when her brother came, so he joined her there. Where the "table" was a place of refreshing, the "study" was a sanctuary. There his sister was able to minister to his wounded heart. Because of the comfort she had received, she was able to minister to his pain and deliver with confidence the same "product" that she had experienced. He received Jesus on that visit and has been walking out his salvation ever since.

I look back with fondness and reverence to those days when I sat around his table. Most of the time I did not visit for any specific reason. To me it was like the tabernacle of David—a sanctuary. Jesus showed up in that place because He tabernacled with that man as He desires to do with all other men and women. At that table, I learned the most valuable lesson of my life, that Jesus lives in me in the good times as well as the fractured everyday experiences, which are common to man. He is never far off.

Maybe just a cup away.

CHAPTER 16

Milk Is a Four-Letter Word
Conclusion

"I have come to think that Pastor Al Isaksen is the finest minister I have ever known, because he interferes with God the least."

Jim Kinnier

Milk has gotten a good deal of attention throughout history. It is quite popular. Try Google and you will have the choice of more than half a billion options. It certainly affects us all. That is because of relationship. We have all had a personal experience with it in some way. Some have a great association with milk, lauding its taste and nutritional value. Others become irate at the mention of it, linking it with all sorts of health issues and even death.

Wikipedia describes it as "an opaque, white liquid that provides the primary source of nutrition for newborns before they are able to digest other types of food."

Other sources call it a "poison." They say that it is filled with nasty additives, antibiotics, steroids, or it's just plain indigestible.

Not too much praise from that crowd. So how do we account for the vast difference? Is milk the culprit, or the commodity?

Is it the milk that causes differing effects, or is it the one who receives it? No doubt both answers could be at least partially correct. Perhaps there is a third possibility, though: contamination. Of course, this is not breaking news in investigative journalism. Everyone knows that milk has been tampered with and that ingredients have been added, as well as subtracted. Sick cows are sometimes milked, and much can happen between the udder and the shelf to interfere with a healthy product.

I can remember drinking a cold glass of milk that made me feel strong, and I can remember drinking a gulp of spoiled milk that gave me convulsions. It didn't break my relationship with the product. It simply made me a bit cautious. I suppose that if I were poisoned I would have a different outlook completely. Milk and I would not occupy the same space any longer.

I think that is how it is with the gospel. Some look forward to their next glass with anticipation. Others disdain the thought. Still more (and I believe this group is large in number) might accept a glass on occasion but in general have no interest. To them "milk is for kids or old people." So is the Bible. So is church. Perhaps Wikipedia is correct in its definition that milk is primarily for newborns. If milk is not an option, then what is? If "milk" is a metaphor for the gospel, then why is it that so many have found it to be so undesirable? I suppose the bigger question is if the gospel is what it claims to be—that is, the "Word of God"—why is it so boring and irrelevant? How can it be that the Designer and Creator of this unfathomable, fast-moving universe could bring forth anything that is boring?

Which leads me back to the third possibility, and that is contamination. Something has gotten into the milk. This is not a new phenomenon, but its vast effect has grown enormously. A few years ago, China became the object of international attention from the exposure of the nation's milk industry. In order to increase its profit, milk producers added a chemical known as melamine. It is a white substance that had widespread use in the American kitchen as well. The difference is that American factories have used it to fabricate cheap kitchen cabinets, while Chinese milk producers have used it to furnish the contents of a baby's bottle. As a result, thousands of infants have been hospitalized and many have tragically died due to the reckless alteration of a natural and trusted product. Once digested, the poison began its destructive work in these tiny, vulnerable newborns, whose future became tenuous. The economic effect of manufactured greed became a blight to milk producers across the planet.

So it has been with the gospel. As with milk, the gospel has been contaminated. That which was introduced as an attractive thirst-quenching, soul-strengthening, and life-giving substance has been discovered to be poisonous by many over the years.

People have been exposed to the gospel for centuries, and for centuries it has given men and women inspiration to live creatively and courageously. The redemption story has been the inspiration for writers, poets, artists, and statesman throughout the world. It has crossed deserts and oceans, mountains and jungles by selfless men and women, without any motivation other than the desire to spread its life-changing message.

Without its ring of freedom in a world of sorrows, where would writers like Victor Hugo, Tolstoy, Dostoyevsky, or Solzhenitsyn get their message of love and purpose amidst gray and meaningless surroundings? Where would John Bunyan discover a journey in life that was paved with danger and hardship, and yet believe the reward beyond was worth every effort here to persevere? What about the slaves? From where did their song arise? What mountaintop did Martin Luther King, Jr., visit if not the one he visited in the pages of the Book? Why does the message of *Les Miserables* ring so true to the experience of man? What kind of love is it that converts an incorrigible wretch into a selfless hero, who has left audiences cheering for decades?

Where did they find their source, and from what fountain did they drink in order to gain such strength for the human soul? What made them capable of displaying this quality that can inspire another to see what he or she had never seen before?

Was it "contaminated milk" that caused the Pilgrims to leave homes and properties, families and occupations? Where did they capture the will to persevere after having buried wives, husbands, and children?

For what reason would countless men and women across the globe risk imprisonment, torture, and even death for the sake of a belief?

No, this was the real thing, pure Milk, the kind that was once delivered to the saints for all time. It was preserved and delivered from generation to generation. Faithful men and women inspired others to become faithful men and women. They delivered a simple unadulterated message of inward transformation, which produced outward courage that has repeatedly affected their cultures in positive ways.

The gospel was delivered in the same way in which it was received, pure and unhampered. It was expected of the milkman with his product, as it should be from every pastor with the gospel.

It seems, however, that a lot has changed.

The milk is different, and so is the milkman. He is missing. In fact, there is a fading generation that cannot even recall the days when the milkman delivered.

I can.

Jesus did not die in vain. He prayed while He was here for the Father's will to be done. His prayers *will* all be answered; His church *will* be built. It *will* be filled with believers from every tribe, nation, tongue, and people, Jew and Gentile alike. One day He *will* return for a Bride. She *will* have made herself ready. It *will* be a glorious day like no other.

My heart's cry is the same as Pastor Al's, as well as that of Jesus.

If you as a pastor are called to deliver His product, keep it pure.

It is already perfect.

Do not add. Do not subtract.

You are dear to Him who called you. Though your struggles are real, your purpose is greater.

Let your heart be broken so that you might join with Him once again in sincerity and in truth. Let nothing get in your way. Dismiss the religious spirit at every turn. The world is crying for authenticity and power. Hear their cry and make it personal to your message.

His return is nigh, and there will soon be no time for regret.

Respond now to the urgent cry of the Spirit of the Almighty God.

And make a difference.

You were designed for that and you know it.

Pastor Al and Dorothy, the Milkman and his bride

COMMENTS ABOUT PASTOR AL

"I will NEVER forget the first time I heard him preach and teach. During his anointed message from Heaven he spoke about Jesus in a way that touched and changed me and my relationship with Jesus forever!"

Pastor Jim Barca
Hempstead, NY

"How can I write a couple of lines about someone who has changed my life forever??"

Debbie Dufek
New Baltimore, NY

"How many pastors came out of that church? I could give a list of names of people I know personally whose ministries began as the result of sitting under his teaching. The prophecy over it was that it would be a 'feeding station,' and truly it was. Being the only charismatic church in Suffolk County at that time, people came from all over. They came in jeans with bare feet and hungry hearts. Sunday and Tuesday mornings were always full because no one wanted to miss something."

Fairlee Pasfield
Florida

"His countenance expressed the assurance of his security in the Lord Jesus. His warm electrifying smile spoke aloud of his joy in The Lord."

Joan Preston
MIddle Island NY

"After attending a seminar in Moody Bible College with Pastor Al, I remember thinking to myself that he should have been at the podium—he was a far better teacher than all of them!"

Ed Gertz
Evington, VA

"God has used Pastor Al (and Dorothy) in my life to bring me great freedom, peace and joy."

Jane Dil Iulio
Oklahoma

"We went to church knowing we might be stirred (by God's Spirit) to share a Scripture, song or testimony. We went to minister as well as receive. We dined in each other's homes and were involved in each other's lives because we truly cared for each other."

Luanne Austin
Harrisonburg, VA

"What does a man look like when he believes the Bible to be the Word of God and believes Jesus is both Savior and Lord? He looks like Pastor Al. Many say the same but don't live it. He did."

Pastor Dennis Hodulick
Bayshore, NY

CONCLUSION

Actually once *you* enter the milkman story, there is no end.
The story keeps going.

That is the intention of this book.

Join us at
TheMilkmanStory.com